walc™

Workbook of Activities for Language and Cognition

Linda Bowers
Rosemary Huisingh
Paul F. Johnson
Carolyn LoGiudice
Jane Orman

Skill Area:	Problem Solving
Ages:	Adults

LinguiSystems, Inc.
3100 4th Avenue
East Moline, IL 61244-9700

E-Mail: service@linguisystems.com
Web: linguisystems.com
Fax: 800-577-4555

800-776-4332

Printed in the U.S.A.
ISBN 0-7606-0476-2

About the Authors

Rosemary Huisingh, M.A., CCC-SLP, is a LinguiSystems co-owner and co-author of many therapy and testing materials including *Expressive Language Kit*, *Expressive Language Test*, *TOPS Kit—Adolescent*, *TOPS—Adolescent Test*, *WORD Test-R (Elementary)*, and *ACHIEV-Revised*.

Jane Orman, M.A., CCC-SLP, is a test developer and customer care representative for LinguiSystems. She is co-author of many testing and therapy materials including *WORD Kit—Elementary*, *WORD Test-R (Elementary)*, *Expressive Language Test*, *Listening Test*, *Listening Kit*, *TOPS Kit—Elementary*, *TOPS-R (Elementary) Test*, and *Just for Adults Reading Comprehension*.

Paul F. Johnson, B.A., is an editor and writer for LinguiSystems and the author of many LinguiSystems titles, including *125 Ways to Be a Better Writer*, *WRITEopoly*, *Category Scramble*, *50 Quick Play Language Games*, and *Word Scramble*.

Carolyn LoGiudice, M.S., CCC-SLP, is an editor, writer, and acquisitions coordinator for LinguiSystems. She is co-author of numerous therapy and testing materials including *That's Life! Social Language Skills*, *100% Grammar*, *100% Grammar LITE*, *100% Punctuation*, *Expressive Language Kit*, *Expressive Language Test*, and *Grammar Play by Play*.

Linda Bowers, M.A., CCC-SLP, is a LinguiSystems co-owner and co-author of many therapy and testing materials including *Grammar Scramble*, *Expressive Language Kit*, *Expressive Language Test*, *TOPS Kit—Adolescent*, *TOPS—Adolescent Test*, and *ACHIEV-Revised*.

FVh
1.00

Table of Contents

Introduction 4

Section One

Unit 1: Problem Solving 5

Unit 2: Analyzing Problems 17

Unit 3: Understanding & Applying Information 39

Unit 4: Paraphrasing & Summarizing 51

Unit 5: Making Inferences 63

Unit 6: Empathizing 75

Unit 7: Evaluating 87

Section Two

Unit 8: General Problem Solving 99

Answer Key 180

Introduction

The authors who have created this book have varied backgrounds, but they have one thing in common: each is committed to building and enhancing cognitive skills. The abilities to reason, to think critically, and to problem solve not only enhance our ability to survive, they also enhance our lives. Someone who has temporarily lost these skills due to a brain trauma will benefit from the activities in these pages in a variety of ways. Not only will your clients begin to relearn the cognitive survival skills they have lost, but they may eventually enhance their previous skills by systematically rebuilding them on a stronger foundation.

The activities in *Walc 3* are split into two sections. The first section (Units 1-7) includes isolated practice in the following skills:

- Identifying Problems & Generating Solutions
- Analyzing Problems
- Understanding & Applying Information
- Paraphrasing & Summarizing
- Making Inferences
- Empathizing
- Evaluating

In addition to the breakdown of skill areas, the situations are also separated by interest areas: Money, Work, Family & Social Relationships, Health & Safety, and Sports & Leisure. Each page of the first section of the book is coded with a symbol in the upper left-hand corner of the page to guide you. You might find that matching these interest areas with those of your clients will produce even more successful results.

The second section of the book (Unit 8) includes practice in integrating the cognitive and problem-solving skills included in the first section. Each situation includes a photograph and brief story, much like you'd find in a newspaper, followed by several questions about the passage. This type of practice allows your clients to use the isolated skills they've already practiced in the book along with their own experiences to respond to a real-life situation.

We hope this book will help your clients rebuild their problem-solving and cognitive skills and enhance their quality of life in the process. Good luck!

1 Problem Solving

Money

Work

Family & Social Relationships

Health & Safety

Sports & Leisure

Poor problem solvers, or those who have lost their ability to break a problem into its components, often skip the most essential step in the process. No problem can benefit from a successful resolution if it isn't clearly defined.

Most problems are very clear. If you are having lunch with a friend and she begins choking on a piece of chicken, you know what the problem is—food is blocking her airway. Once you've identified the problem, you can immediately begin working toward a solution.

Other problems aren't so clear. On a different day, you're having lunch with another friend, and something seems wrong. There is tension between the two of you. You're both cordial, you have polite conversation, but you know something isn't right. What's the problem here? Is your friend angry at you for something? Is your friend preoccupied with another problem? Or is everything actually fine with your friend and might something else be subconsciously bothering you?

Approaching this problem requires you to think carefully about what the problem is as you perceive it. Once you clearly state the problem in your own words, you can begin working toward a solution. In this case, the problem might be stated, "There may be a problem between my friend and me." This is a simple statement, but it opens the door to the generation of several possible solutions or further analysis.

In this unit, you'll practice identifying a clear problem statement based on a brief scenario. Then you will use the information from the problem statement to generate a solution that you think will work best. As you move through the book, you'll practice analyzing problems at a deeper level; but for now, simply generate a quick solution for each problem based on the limited information you have.

Problem Solving

1. You own your house and enjoy caring for it. You need to make some emergency repairs but you don't have enough money in your savings account.

   What is the problem?
   a. You have the money, but it's expected to rain this weekend.
   b. You can make the repairs but you need another person to help you.
   c. You don't have enough money to fix the house right now.

   What should you do?
   a. Make the repairs yourself regardless of expense.
   b. Put the repairs on a credit card and hope you can pay for it later.
   c. Call a reputable home repair company, make all the repairs now, and ask the company to let you make payments as your income allows.

2. A man from a window company stops by your house. The company is offering a 50% discount if you sign the contract and give them a $100 deposit today.

   What is the problem?
   a. You need new windows.
   b. The company may not be reputable.
   c. The man is not wearing a tie.

   What should you do?
   a. Call friends or the Better Business Bureau to find out if the company is reputable.
   b. Write the representative a check for $100.
   c. Find out if they have the window you need.

3. You received a credit card application that offers lower rates for customers over 65. You have a limited income. If you get the card, you will have six credit cards.

   What is the problem?
   a. You need another credit card.
   b. Another credit card may cause you to go too deeply into debt.
   c. The company has a lower rate for people under 65.

   What is the solution?
   a. Sign and send the application immediately.
   b. Call the company and accuse them of targeting seniors.
   c. Do a budget to determine if you can get another card.

Problem Solving

4. You planned well for your retirement and have enough spendable income to live as you wish. Recently, several family members have asked for loans.

   Problem: ______________________________

   ____

   Solution: ______________________________

   ____

5. Your daughter is a full-time student and works nights. She wants to buy a house but can't make the down payment requirements. She's asked you for help in making the down payment.

   Problem: ______________________________

   ____

   Solution: ______________________________

   ____

6. The IRS is going to audit your tax return for the year you retired. You've never gone through an audit.

   Problem: ______________________________

   ____

   Solution: ______________________________

   ____

7. The doctor you've gone to for years is dropping her affiliation from your insurance plan. You don't want to change doctors but you need the cost advantage of the insurance.

   Problem: ______________________________

   ____

   Solution: ______________________________

   ____

Problem Solving

1. You work at home running a catering business. The codes of your town have changed so that you are no longer able to run a commercial business in a residential neighborhood.

   What is the problem?

   a. You can't run your catering business from your home anymore.
   b. You need a new kitchen.
   c. You need to hire more employees.

   What should you do?

   a. Complain to your friends that the world's unfair.
   b. Keep operating your business and hope no one says anything.
   c. Consider looking for a new place to live in a commercial zone.

2. You have just returned to work after a long illness. Your boss seems distant and cold about your return and he assigns you work you're not familiar with.

   What is the problem?

   a. You want to be friends with your boss.
   b. The company doesn't pay you enough.
   c. You're confused by your boss' behavior and don't know what to do.

   What should you do?

   a. Complain to a co-worker about your problem.
   b. Ask for an appointment to speak with your boss about your confusion.
   c. Quit your job.

3. You have returned to work after having a stroke. You still have a slight speech defect that makes your speech slurred.

   What is the problem?

   a. You dribble on your chin when you drink coffee.
   b. You can't talk fast enough.
   c. People might have difficulty understanding your speech.

   What should you do?

   a. Explain to people about your speech and do your best to make yourself understood.
   b. Ignore people's reactions to you.
   c. Don't drink coffee.

Problem Solving

4. Since you need the assistance of a cane to walk, your physician has advised you to stay home from work on icy days.

   Problem: ____

   ____

   Solution: ____

   ____

5. Your company has a toll-free number for customer service. At least once a week, your daughter uses this toll-free number to call you at work to chat.

   Problem: ____

   ____

   Solution: ____

   ____

6. You and your spouse do word-processing and graphic design from your home. You have many clients coming to your house to pick up their work. The constant foot traffic through the house bothers your young daughter.

   Problem: ____

   ____

   Solution: ____

   ____

7. Your boss asks you to play golf with him. You've already made plans that day but don't want to offend your boss by refusing.

   Problem: ____

   ____

   Solution: ____

   ____

Problem Solving

1. For 30 years you have prepared the traditional Thanksgiving dinner for the 24 members of your family. You haven't been feeling well lately, and Thanksgiving is just two weeks away.

   What is the problem?

   a. You don't want to prepare the Thanksgiving dinner.
   b. You think it's time someone else took a turn for a change.
   c. You don't think you are physically well enough to prepare the dinner.

   What should you do?

   a. Ask another family member to prepare and host the dinner.
   b. Order out from a fast-food restaurant.
   c. Cancel the traditional dinner.

2. Your grandson comes back to your town from college about once a month. You write to him every week, but he doesn't stop to see you when he's home.

   What is the problem?

   a. Your grandson misses you.
   b. You feel he owes it to you to stop and see you when he's in town.
   c. Your grandson never comes home.

   What should you do?

   a. In your next letter, ask your grandson to call you.
   b. Stop writing.
   c. Complain to his mother that he never visits anymore.

3. A friend is visiting you at your house one afternoon. The doorbell rings and your eight-year-old grandson and his dog are at the door. Your friend doesn't like dogs.

   What is the problem?

   a. The dog doesn't want to play with your guest.
   b. The dog's paws are too muddy.
   c. If the dog comes in, your guest will feel uncomfortable.

   What should you do?

   a. Ask your guest to leave immediately.
   b. Ask your grandson to take the dog to the backyard.
   c. Make sure the dog stays quiet when he comes inside your house.

Problem Solving

4. You'd like to invite a group of eight friends to come over for lunch and card games. You know that two of the women don't like each other very much.

   Problem: ____

   ____

   Solution: ____

   ____

5. Your son and daughter and their families gather once a month at your house to eat dinner and watch a video. Usually all four of your grandchildren bring friends who are noisy and rambunctious.

   Problem: ____

   ____

   Solution: ____

   ____

6. Your next door neighbor's son parks his rusty old car in front of your house most of the time. You are mortified by its dirty appearance.

   Problem: ____

   ____

   Solution: ____

   ____

7. You spent most of yesterday planting flowers in your garden. This morning you open the curtains and the plants are uprooted or broken off. You see the neighbor's dog rolling in your flower bed.

   Problem: ____

   ____

   Solution: ____

   ____

Problem Solving

1. While you're watching TV one night, you feel a sharp pain in your arm and you're suddenly short of breath.

   What is the problem?

   a. You have indigestion.
   b. You might be having a heart attack.
   c. You've broken a bone in your hand.

   What should you do?

   a. Call 911.
   b. Relax and wait for it to pass.
   c. Start waving your arm around until it starts to feel normal again.

2. Your doctor suggests you need to become more physically active. He advises that you take up a low-impact, nonstrenuous sport.

   What is the problem?

   a. You are getting plenty of exercise.
   b. You aren't getting enough exercise.
   c. You're getting too much exercise.

   What should you do?

   a. Take up handball.
   b. Take up jogging.
   c. Take up walking.

3. Your kitchen has a linoleum floor. You have fallen twice in your kitchen in the past year.

   What is the problem?

   a. Someone keeps mopping the floor and not telling you it's wet.
   b. The linoleum is too slick.
   c. There is too much foot traffic in your kitchen.

   What should you do?

   a. Keep your kitchen floors waxed.
   b. Keep your floors cleaner.
   c. Have your kitchen floor carpeted or replaced with wood.

Problem Solving

4. You have an eye doctor appointment at the same time as your dental appointment.

   Problem: ______________________________

   ____

   Solution: ______________________________

   ____

5. You're looking out your front window and you see a two-year-old neighbor girl walking down the street all by herself. Her parents are nowhere to be seen.

   Problem: ______________________________

   ____

   Solution: ______________________________

   ____

6. A friend tells you he's developed a rigorous workout regimen. You remind him to consult his doctor before beginning the program. He waves you off and tells you he's not worried about it.

   Problem: ______________________________

   ____

   Solution: ______________________________

   ____

7. You're eating lunch with a friend. He suddenly stops talking, his face turns red, and he begins pointing at his throat.

   Problem: ______________________________

   ____

   Solution: ______________________________

   ____

Problem Solving

1. You want to send a birthday invitation to an old friend who has just moved to a different apartment. You don't know his new address but you do know the phone number.

   What is the problem?

   a. You don't know which bus to take to visit your friend.
   b. You miss your friend.
   c. You don't know where your friend lives now.

   What should you do?

   a. Write a letter to your friend and ask for the new address.
   b. Call your friend. Ask for the new address.
   c. Wait for your friend to call you.

2. After a plane flight, you wait in the baggage claim area and watch other passengers from your flight collect their luggage. Your suitcase doesn't show up.

   What is the problem?

   a. You need a new suitcase.
   b. You don't have the clothes and items you brought for the trip.
   c. You'll have to take someone else's suitcase instead.

   What should you do?

   a. Report your missing suitcase to the appropriate airline.
   b. Take someone else's suitcase.
   c. Cancel the rest of your trip.

3. Your friend's daughter is on a volleyball team. As she tells you about her game today, she uses words like *spike* and *kill*. You're not sure what she means.

   What is the problem?

   a. You think she might have killed someone with a spike.
   b. You're sure someone on the volleyball team must be seriously injured.
   c. You are not familiar with these volleyball terms.

   What should you do?

   a. Call the police to report the crime.
   b. Ask her what the words mean.
   c. Tell her parents their daughter is acting strangely.

Problem Solving

4. A neighbor invites you over to see his prize-winning orchid collection. His orchids will be in a contest later today. As you examine one plant closely, you sneeze and break off one of the flowers.

   Problem: ______________________________

   ____

   Solution: ______________________________

   ____

5. You're in a stadium to watch your favorite team play. The people in front of you keep standing up and yelling at the players. They are also sloshing their drinks as they wave their arms around.

   Problem: ______________________________

   ____

   Solution: ______________________________

   ____

6. You and a friend are watching a movie in a theater. The language in the movie offends you. You don't want to watch the rest of the movie.

   Problem: ______________________________

   ____

   Solution: ______________________________

   ____

7. You have received two dinner invitations for the same evening. Both of the invitations are from good friends.

   Problem: ______________________________

   ____

   Solution: ______________________________

   ____

Problem Solving

8. You and a friend are at a shopping mall. You each go your separate way to do some shopping. You can't remember where you're supposed to meet your friend, but you remember what time to meet.

   Problem: ______________________________

   ____

   Solution: ______________________________

   ____

9. You are traveling in a rental car on a road miles away from a town. You get a flat tire. You look for the jack, but you can't find it. You have never driven this make of car before.

   Problem: ______________________________

   ____

   Solution: ______________________________

   ____

10. You and your spouse want to enjoy some vacation time together. Your spouse wants to enjoy shows and nightlife. You want to get up early and take walks in quiet, natural surroundings.

    Problem: ______________________________

    ____

    Solution: ______________________________

    ____

11. Most evenings, neighborhood boys play touch football on the street outside your window. They have a habit of yelling and cursing excessively.

    Problem: ______________________________

    ____

    Solution: ______________________________

    ____

2 Analyzing Problems

Money

Work

Family & Social Relationships

Health & Safety

Sports & Leisure

Many people describe themselves as *intuitive* problem solvers. They see a problem; they trust their gut feeling; they immediately put a solution into motion. When this hasty approach to problem solving happens to work, it's usually because the problem is very easy, or you just got lucky. This "Ready, FIRE, aim" approach to problem solving is rarely useful, and people who employ it would more accurately be described as *impulsive* rather than *intuitive*.

Good problem solvers take the time to *analyze* a problem that comes their way. Before reacting with impulsivity to something such as an overdue notice on a bill, a Closed sign on a store, or a lost hotel reservation, a good problem solver takes a moment to examine all that is happening in the situation before reacting. For example, in the case of a lost hotel reservation, an experienced problem solver might consider these (often obvious but overlooked) factors:

- Am I in the right hotel on the right day?
- Does someone else know the reservation system better? Could he/she help me?
- Do I have the proper documentation to prove my reservation?
- I understand that this type of thing happens often and is almost always resolved to the customer's satisfaction. I'm not the first person in the world to face this problem!

The last factor is an important one in analyzing a problem—realizing that what you're facing probably isn't unique. There is a solution available, and finding it is a matter of taking the proper steps.

In this unit, you'll practice answering questions about the details of several problems. As you work through the exercises, challenge yourself to think of other details present in each situation that might help you solve the problems.

Analyzing Problems

Read this page of a phone bill and answer the questions that follow.

Previous Balance	Payment Received	Total Credits	Balance Forward	Adjustments	Current Balance	Total Amt. Due
31.52	31.52 -	0.00	0.00	0.00	37.47	37.47

Billing period 8/01 - 8/31

Previous Balance 31.52
Payments Received Through 7/31 . . . . 31.52
Balance Forward 0.00
Adjustments 0.00
Monthly Charges 32.01
Local Tax 1.16
State Tax 3.04
Federal Tax 1.26
Total Amount Due by 9/15 . . . . 37.47

For questions/concerns regarding your account, please call 1-555-555-2000.

1. How much money do you owe the phone company for the month of August?
   a. $21.52
   b. $33.01
   c. $37.47

2. Do you owe any money from previous bills? Yes _____ No _____

3. Why are the amounts in the Current Balance and Total Amount Due boxes the same?

____

____

Analyzing Problems

Read this bank statement and answer the questions that follow.

BANKING INSTITUTION OF AMERICA, INC.
1200 Tress Street
Richmond, VA 01997
1-555-555-5482

Dear Customer,

An ATM charge of $ __3.00__ has been applied to your account (0123456789) due to out-of-area service fees. If you have any questions or concerns, please contact Mr. Hank R. Crumb.

Thank you.

1. Why is the bank charging you $3.00?
   a. The bank just feels like it.
   b. It's for out-of-area service fees.
   c. You are overdrawn $3.00 on your account.

2. What do you think an out-of-area service fee might be?

   ____

3. Which one of the following situations could explain the $3.00 fee?
   a. You wrote a check for groceries for more money than you had in your account.
   b. You were on vacation and had to withdraw money from a bank that was not the Banking Institution of America, Inc.
   c. The bank is merging with another bank and charging all customers $3.00.

Analyzing Problems

Your 401(k) retirement plan account at work has about $2000 in it. Under the plan's rules, you are allowed to borrow up to 10% of the balance. Your energy bill for a cold winter month is due in a week and you don't have a lot of cash on hand. The bill is $189.

1. If you borrowed the money from your 401(k) plan, would you have enough to pay the energy bill?
   a. no, because there are penalties associated with borrowing
   b. yes, because it's under 20%
   c. yes, because your bill is $189 and you can borrow up to $200

2. Your company advises you not to borrow this money from your 401(k) plan. What do you need to ask to understand why they are saying this?
   a. "Why don't you want me to borrow my own money?"
   b. "What are the pros and cons to borrowing the money?"
   c. "Can I take the day off to go and pay my energy bill?"

3. What could you do to avoid having to borrow from your retirement account in the future?

   ____

   ____

You and your spouse are moving from your house into a smaller apartment. You are looking at two apartments that you like. The first is a one-bedroom that rents for $400 per month. The other is a two-bedroom that is $550 per month. You have three grown children with families. Each family visits about twice a year and they like to stay with you.

1. What are the advantages of taking the larger apartment over the smaller one?

   ____

   ____

2. If you and your spouse really like the smaller apartment, what can you do when your children's families visit?

   ____

   ____

Analyzing Problems

Read this receipt and answer the questions that follow.

Frank's Records

1942 Columbia Street
555-1350

2/16 2:25 PM Store 130

Qty.		Item	Price
1	Pixies - Surfer Blanca	0713	13.99
2	Best of Count Basie	6321	2/9.99
1	Ellery Eskelin - Jazz Noise	4207	17.99

SUBTOTAL	51.96
TAX	4.95
TOTAL	56.91
Cash	60.00
Change	3.09

1. What store is this receipt from?

 ____

2. How were the records paid for?
 a. cash
 b. credit card
 c. traveler's check

3. Which record did the customer buy two of?
 a. Pixies
 b. Count Basie
 c. Ellery Eskelin

Analyzing Problems

You see the following listing in a local college bulletin for a computer class you'd like to take. Your company offers a 100% tuition reimbursement benefit. Read this bulletin and answer the questions that follow.

Microsoft Word Class

Join the computer world! In this class, you'll learn to set up pages and create, edit, save, and print documents. You'll also learn to use various menu functions such as inserting, formatting, and editing to create or modify documents. This class is limited to 15 students.

Fee: $495
Days: M-T-Th
Time: 5:30-7:30 p.m.
Dates: Oct 1-Oct 22
Site: Mink Community College
Teacher: staff

1. How much will the class cost you? ______________________

2. How many days will the class meet each week? ______________________

3. On what date will the class end? ______________________

4. How many hours will you be in class per week? ______________________

5. Where will the class meet? ______________________

6. Will you learn to type? ______________________

7. How many students will be in the class? ______________________

Analyzing Problems

As a real estate agent, you get a 7% commission for selling a house. You recently sold a house for $200,000, which was $12,000 less than the asking price. The buyer will pay the closing costs and other fees amounting to about $2,500.

1. What was the selling price of the house?

   ____

2. As the agent, what will you get?

   ____

3. How much did the seller get?

   ____

4. How much will the buyer pay totally?

   ____

Late Friday, your boss asks you to prepare a report for her which she needs for a meeting next Thursday morning. She wants the report by noon Wednesday to review. You know the report will take a full day and a half to prepare. Sunday afternoon you get the flu and are unable to go to the office on Monday.

1. How much time does your boss want to review the report?

   ____

2. If you start on the report immediately at 8 a.m. on Tuesday, what's the earliest you will have the report ready?

   ____

3. If you can't work on the report at the office, where's another place you might finish it?

   ____

Analyzing Problems

Read the following classified ad and answer the questions that follow.

300 HELP WANTED

SALESPERSON — AJAC Teleservices. Our top salespeople earn $350-$450 per week. Average salespeople earn $280 per week. Hot market! Products in the mortgage and financial industry. Excellent benefits for full-time employees after 90 days. Paid weekly. Only professional, mature individuals need apply. 1st and 2nd shifts available. Please call 1-800-322-3562, ext 246, or fax 1-800-322-8992.

1. What will you sell? ______________________________

2. How could you find out more information about the products? ______________

3. What can a top-notch salesperson expect to make in a month? ______________

4. What kind of benefits do full-time salespeople receive? ______________

5. If you're an average salesperson, what will you make each week? ______________

Analyzing Problems

You manage an apartment complex with 50 two-bedroom and 75 three-bedroom apartments. The smaller units rent for $375 per month and the larger ones are $500 per month. Each apartment requires a one year lease. Prior to moving in, renters must pay one month's rent and a one month deposit equal to one month's rent. Housebroken pets are allowed for an extra $150 deposit. Two references are required. There is a laundromat in the apartment complex.

1. How many apartments do you have to oversee? ______________________

2. How much does a two-bedroom unit rent for per month? ______________________

3. How much does it cost to rent a three-bedroom unit for a year? ______________________

4. What does it cost to have a pet at this complex? ______________________

5. What is the deposit for the smaller apartment? ______________________

6. How many references must a renter have? ______________________

7. Where can a renter do laundry? ______________________

8. What is the deposit for the larger apartment? ______________________

9. If a renter wants to rent an apartment for six months, will you let him? ______________________

10. How many two-bedroom apartments do you have to manage? ______________________

11. A potential renter calls you and says she'd like to rent out a larger apartment. She says she has $900 and is ready to move in tomorrow. You say no. Why?

    ____

    ____

    ____

Analyzing Problems

You're recently divorced and would like to begin dating again. You see the following newspaper ad that interests you. Answer the questions that follow.

> **Need Someone to Talk to?**
>
> Call 1-900-555-1111
>
> $2.00 for the first minute and $.50 for each additional minute
>
> Minimum of one minute charge
>
> Meet friends in the area
>
> Listen to personal ads
>
> **Call today!**

1. What's the least amount of time you can be charged for a call?
   a. one minute
   b. two minutes
   c. three minutes

2. What's the least amount of money this call will cost you?
   a. $2.00
   b. $2.50
   c. $3.00

3. The ad says that you will be able to meet people from where?
   a. locally
   b. from any state
   c. from around the world

Analyzing Problems

You want to buy a coat from a catalog for a family member. Here's the information you see:

Insulated Wool Parka	SYD'S CLOTHES CATALOG
Description Zip-front Full-length 100% Wool Shell 100% Polyester Lining and Insulation	
Sizes Men's: S M L XL Women's: S M L XL (1-800-555-2222 for Big & Tall Sizes)	
Colors Black Teal Navy Blue Red Gold	
Price $69.99 (order more than one for $59.95 each — Save $10 per item!)	

1. How many sizes can you choose from? ______________________________

2. What number do you need to call about larger sizes? ______________________________

3. How many parkas do you have to order to get the discount? ____________________

4. How much would you save if you bought three coats? ______________________________

5. Is it possible to buy a purple parka? ______________________________

6. The family member wants a fleece-lined parka. Is this the one for him? ______________

Analyzing Problems

You want to schedule a family picture. You see this ad in the newspaper.

> **Goldman Studios**
>
> *Fine Family and Professional Portraits*
>
> Monday thru Friday
> 10 a.m.-5 p.m.
>
> Call for evening and weekend appointments.
>
> ✓ $45.00 sitting fee, refunded at time of portrait package purchase
> ✓ 50 print package available from $139.95, including free 11"x14"
>
> 5656 Verde Street
>
> 555-3434

1. How many hours is the studio open each day?
   a. six
   b. seven
   c. eight

2. What's the lowest cost package you can purchase? ______________________

3. How many pictures are included in the package? ______________________

4. How much extra do you pay for the 11"x14"? ______________________

5. How much is the sitting fee? ______________________

6. What do you need to do in order to have your picture taken on the weekend? ____________

____

Analyzing Problems

You and a friend have lunch together. The server gives you your check.

LOU'S DINER
564 Shorn Blvd.
555-6539

Clerk 003 Date: 11/10

Item	*Qty*	*Price*
Chicken Salad Sandwich	1	5.50
Iced Tea	1	.85
Soup and Salad	1	4.95
Coffee	1	.65
	Subtotal	11.95
	Tax	.87
	Amount Due	12.82
	Check	12.82

Thank you!

1. What is the total you have to pay?
   a. $11.95
   b. $5.50
   c. $12.82

2. How much was the tax? ______________________

3. What was the more expensive meal? ______________________

4. About how much would you tip the food server if you left 20%? ______________________

Analyzing Problems

Read this prescription and answer the questions that follow.

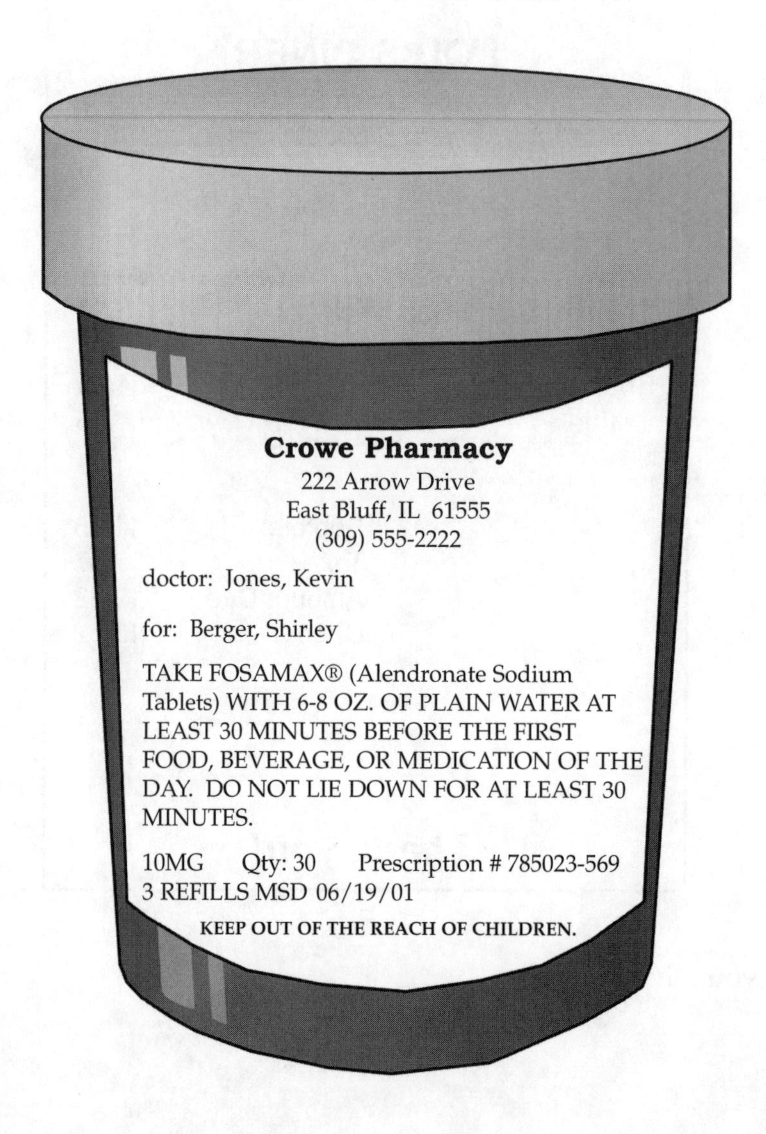

1. What is this medicine called?
   a. Kevin Jones
   b. Fosamax®
   c. Crowe

Analyzing Problems

2. Who is this prescription for?
   a. Kevin Jones
   b. Fosamax®
   c. Shirley Berger

3. Which doctor prescribed the medicine?
   a. Dr. Crowe
   b. Dr. Jones
   c. Dr. Berger

4. How many tablets are in this prescription?
   a. 10
   b. 20
   c. 30

5. Can this prescription be refilled? ____________ If so, how many times? _______________

6. What does Shirley need to know to order a refill of this medicine?

   ____

7. What time should Shirley take the medicine?

   ____

8. Should Shirley use coffee or juice to help her swallow one of these tablets? Why or why not?

   ____

   ____

9. Why shouldn't Shirley take this medicine before she goes to bed at night?

   ____

   ____

Analyzing Problems

Read the hospital directory and answer the questions that follow.

Kanga Medical Center
DIRECTORY

Boden, Dr. Peter *Dentist*	**350**
Center for Nutrition	**G100**
Day Care Center	**G25**
Employee Health Office	**150**
Johnson, Dr. Stephen *Internal Medicine*	**325**
Kanga Area Services	**G75**
Kanga Credit Union	**100**
Kanga Laboratory	**125**
Mangili, Dr. Paul *Pediatrics*	**250**
Prenatal Clinic	**G50**
Social Services	**375**
Surgery Center	**225**

1. Where would you go to see Dr. Mangili?
   a. first floor
   b. second floor
   c. third floor

2. Which floor is the Center for Nutrition located on?
   a. ground floor
   b. first floor
   c. second floor

3. Who is the doctor of internal medicine? ______________________________

4. If you needed to go to the Kanga Credit Union and the Kanga Laboratory, would you stay on the same floor? ______________________________

Analyzing Problems

Read this phone message from your doctor and answer the questions that follow.

A.S.A.P.

MESSAGE

To John

From Dr. Walters

Of Mercy General

Telephone

In re: test results

Pager 555-1792

- [ ] TELEPHONED
- [ ] CAME TO SEE YOU
- [x] WANTS TO SEE YOU
- [ ] RETURNED YOUR CALL
- [x] PLEASE CALL
- [ ] WILL CALL AGAIN
- [x] IMPORTANT
- [x] PAGE

Date 4/20 Time 8:52 PM (AM)

1. Who is this message for?
   a. Dr. Walters
   b. John
   c. Mercy General

2. What should you do now that you have received the message. Check one.

   telephone the doctor ________ page the doctor ________

3. Did Dr. Walters call in the morning or the afternoon? ________________

Analyzing Problems

Read the following schedule and answer the questions that follow.

BIG TOWN HIGH SCHOOL FOOTBALL SCHEDULE
1999

Date	Opponent	Location	Time
Aug 24	Valley View	HOME	8:00 PM
Sept 7	Lakeland	AWAY	8:00 PM
Sept 14 (Parent's Day)	Ontario	HOME	8:00 PM
Sept 21	Pleasant Springs	HOME	8:00 PM
Sept 28	Rockstar	AWAY	8:00 PM
Oct 5	Mentville	AWAY	8:00 PM
Oct 12 (Homecoming)	Jefferson	HOME	8:00 PM
Oct 26	Lakeland	HOME	8:00 PM
Nov 2	Fillmore	AWAY	8:00 PM
Nov 9	Hayes	HOME	8:00 PM
Nov 16 (Senior Day)	Spann Town	HOME	8:00 PM
Nov 23	Mayes	AWAY	8:00 PM

Call for tickets! 1-800-555-4758

1. Whose schedule is this?
   a. Big Town's football team
   b. Valley View's team
   c. Big Town's basketball team

Analyzing Problems

2. When do the games start?
   a. eight o'clock at night
   b. eight o'clock in the morning
   c. eight o'clock in the afternoon

3. Who does Big Town play twice?
   a. Lakeland
   b. Spann Town
   c. Mayes

4. What is a homecoming game?
   a. a game where the players go home afterward
   b. a game where alumni come to watch the game and be in a parade
   c. a game where the quarterback yells, "Come home!" to his receivers

5. What season of the year does this schedule cover?
   a. winter
   b. spring
   c. summer
   d. autumn

6. Where would you go to watch the Big Town vs. Ontario game? ______________________

7. On what date does Big Town play Mentville? ______________________

8. What number should you call if you want tickets?
   a. 1-800-555-4759
   b. 1-800-555-4753
   c. 1-800-555-4758

9. Who is Big Town playing on Parent's Day, and what is the date?

   ____

Analyzing Problems

Read this advertisement and answer the questions that follow.

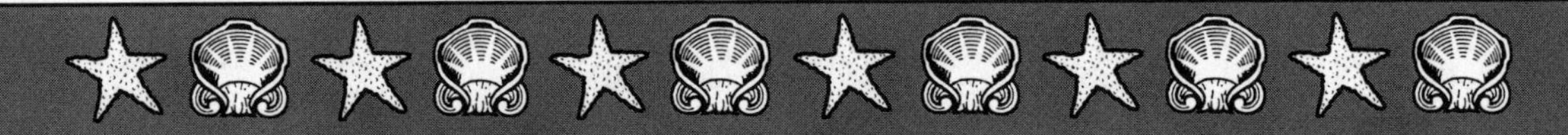

Swanee Beach Resort and Spa

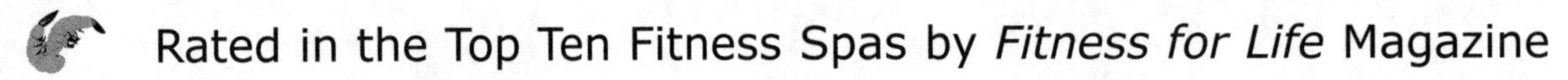

- Rated in the Top Ten Fitness Spas by *Fitness for Life* Magazine
- "Excellent" Rating by *USA Spas and Resorts Journal*
- Five star cuisine rating by Chef Michael of Ritz Restaurant, Miami
- Named "Best Decor" by *Inside Resort* Magazine

We're located in beautiful Swanee, FL, only 30 miles up the coast from Miami.

Weekend packages start at $290 per person. Breakfasts are included.

Prices are based on double occupancy.

All major credit cards accepted.

Call us at 1-800-555-3400, or fax us at 1-800-555-3500.

Make your reservations now!

Analyzing Problems

1. What is this an advertisement for?
   a. restaurant
   b. fitness spa
   c. bed and breakfast

2. Who rated the spa in the top ten of fitness spas?
   a. *Fitness for Life* magazine
   b. *USA Today*
   c. Chef Michael of the Ritz Restaurant

3. What restaurant rating did Swanee Resort's cuisine receive?
   a. ★★★½
   b. ★★★
   c. ★★★★★

4. What is the quality of the decor at this spa? How can you tell?

   ____

   ____

5. What are the ways you can contact this spa?

   ____

6. What does the minimum package cost?

   ____

   ____

7. What does *based on double occupancy* mean?

   ____

   ____

Analyzing Problems

You are going to your daughter's field hockey game today. The gates to the stadium open at 2:00 p.m. and the game starts at 3:00 p.m. Your tickets are in Section F, Row 8, Seats 36 and 37.

1. Who is going to the game?
   a. you and someone else
   b. just you
   c. your son

2. Who is playing in the game?
   a. your son
   b. your daughter
   c. your stepdaughter

3. What seats do you have?
   a. Seats 36 and 37, Row 8, Section F
   b. Seats 36 and 37, Row 19, Section F
   c. Seats 38 and 39, Row 8, Section G

4. What time does the game start?
   a. three o'clock in the afternoon
   b. two o'clock in the afternoon
   c. three o'clock in the morning

5. What time does the stadium open? ______________________________

6. Can you get into the game if you forget your tickets? ______________________

7. Are seats in Row 8 probably farther away or closer to the action? ____________

8. Is field hockey played on ice? ______________________________

9. It's autumn. What type of clothing should you wear to the game?

   ____

3 Understanding & Applying Information

Money

Work

Family & Social Relationships

Health & Safety

Sports & Leisure

As human beings we're plagued by fears. Most of them are small (where did I put my keys!) and others are very serious and deep-rooted (fear of illness or mental incapacity). Somewhere in between these extremes lies a fear almost everyone seems to have these days—the fear of being wrong.

Maybe it's the incredible amount of information that buzzes in and out of our eyes and ears every day that convinces us that we have to be experts at everything! The fear of being wrong causes many problems that could simply be avoided by asking the questions, "What does this mean," or "I don't quite understand that; could you repeat it?" One of the keys to better problem solving is admitting when you need more information or when you simply don't understand all the facets of a complicated problem.

Here's an experiment: ask an impulsive, knee-jerk problem solver to reach into your toolbox and grab you a Rogers open-ended socket driver. I bet he'll hand you a tool and say, "Here you go!" But since there is no such tool, he won't be handing you the right thing. It's a silly example, of course, but close to the point. Being impulsive often results in inaccuracies because you don't really understand the vocabulary or details of the problem you're facing. Good problem solvers take the time to understand *new* information that might be part of the problem.

If you simply smile and nod while a banker, broker, or pension plan administrator talks to you about risk-management, return on investment, or tax-sheltered earnings, you'll find yourself not only unenlightened, but perhaps lighter in the wallet. Successful problem solvers ask for more information about something they know only a little about.

In this unit, you'll identify information that will potentially help you solve problems. You'll also use information you might already know to begin problem solving or problem analysis.

Understanding & Applying Information

1. Your financial advisor suggests you move some of your money from one of your savings accounts to another account to increase your earnings. He says fluctuating interest rates will make you more money than fixed interest rates.

   What is a *fluctuating interest rate*? ______________________________

   What is a *fixed interest rate*? ______________________________

   What will happen if you don't change anything? ______________________________

2. You see an advertisement for a play. The tickets are listed at $30 each. When you buy the tickets, the agent at the box office charges you $96 for three tickets.

   Why do you think she might have charged you $6 more than you expected?

   ____

3. Your grandniece and grandnephew are teenagers and live in another state. You don't know their clothing sizes or preferences for birthday gifts.

   What are some possible gifts you could send that wouldn't require knowing sizes or likes and dislikes?

   ______________________________ ______________________________

   ______________________________ ______________________________

4. You receive your phone bill and see that you have been charged with three long distance calls to the same phone number in Ottawa. You don't know anyone in Ottawa.

   What will happen if you send a note with your check explaining why you aren't paying for the calls to Ottawa?

   ____

5. You receive your bank statement and see that your balance is greater in your checkbook than the bank's balance.

   What might happen if you don't resolve the difference?

   a. You will always have a little more in your account.
   b. You might be overdrawn, and the bank will charge your account an overdraft fee.
   c. You have a good chance to win the lottery with that little extra money.

Understanding & Applying Information

6. Your credit card bill indicates your balance is due December 15, and you have a grace period of five days.

   To avoid finance charges, your check must be received by:

   a. 12/19
   b. 12/20
   c. 12/21
   d. 12/22

   What is a *grace period*? ______________________________

7. You just purchased an electric screwdriver from a catalog with a credit card. There is a limited warranty on the tool. When you receive the screwdriver, you discover that it doesn't work. You call the customer service number in the catalog, but it's disconnected.

   What will you do?

   ____

   ____

8. You plan to purchase a new clothes dryer. You can buy one for $495, with 25% down, and 90 days same as cash; or, you can get one for the same price, with nothing down, and 120 days with no interest.

   Which is the better buy?

   ____

9. You want to buy a phone card. You can purchase a five-minute card for $6.50 or a ten-minute card for $12.50.

   Which is the better buy?

   ____

10. You just bought a new toaster and discovered it is broken. What will you do?

    a. Give it to someone you don't like too much.
    b. Try to make the best toast you can given the circumstances.
    c. Return it to the store where you bought it.

Understanding & Applying Information

1. You want to rearrange your living room, but you aren't sure if you can move all the furniture by yourself.

   What might happen if you try to move the furniture by yourself? Choose two answers.

   a. You could hurt yourself.
   b. The room will be bigger.
   c. It might take a long time.

   How could you move the furniture safely? Choose two answers.

   a. Ask a friend to help you.
   b. Ask a family member to help you.
   c. Hope it moves itself.

2. You and some people you work with are taking a co-worker out to lunch tomorrow.

   What information do you need to know before you go? Choose two answers.

   a. your friend's favorite meal
   b. what time you'll go to lunch
   c. what restaurant you're going to

   What might happen if you don't have the information you need about meeting for lunch? Choose two answers.

   a. You might not make it on time.
   b. You might go to the wrong restaurant.
   c. You might order the wrong food.

3. Your boss asks you to complete a project as soon as you can.

   What are some questions you might ask about the project? Choose two answers.

   a. "When exactly will the project need to be finished?"
   b. "Will I get a raise if I do a good job?"
   c. "Can I get help from co-workers if I need it?"

   What might happen if you don't ask good questions about the project?

   ____

   ____

Understanding & Applying Information

4. You'd like to clean your bathroom today. You realize you don't have any bathroom cleaner in the cupboard. You don't want to take the time to go to the store.

   What is something else you can use to clean the bathroom?

   ____

5. One of your co-workers has a much faster computer than yours. You're using it while she is on vacation. You accidentally open a file that shows the company's confidential salary information for all employees. You know this person shouldn't have this information.

   What might happen if you don't say anything to anyone about this file?

   ____

   ____

   What might happen if you report this information to a supervisor?

   ____

   ____

6. You've been having someone from the neighborhood come in and help you with housework once a week. You think you pay this person very well for the work he does. Over the past couple of weeks, though, you haven't been able to find valuables like an antique pocket watch and some of your jewelry. You've known this person for a long time and have always known him to be very trustworthy.

   What are some things you could do before jumping to conclusions about this person?

   ____

   ____

   ____

   What are some questions you could ask this person about the missing items that wouldn't make him feel defensive?

   ____

   ____

   ____

Understanding & Applying Information

1. You have invited several friends to a dinner party. One friend is a vegetarian, one is allergic to dairy products, and one doesn't like tossed salads. Which foods listed below would be good to serve if you want to fix one meal for all these guests? Choose all appropriate answers.

   a. roast beef
   b. carrots and celery
   c. cottage cheese
   d. mixed fruits
   e. pasta with marinara sauce
   f. shrimp cocktail

2. Your sister loves surprises and family get-togethers. You want to arrange a surprise birthday party for her at your house. What do you need to do to arrange the party for her? Choose all logical answers.

   a. Find out when your sister is available.
   b. Tell your sister about the party.
   c. Decide what to serve.
   d. Invite the guests.
   e. Figure out how to make sure your sister arrives on time without knowing about the party.

3. You were in your friend's wedding party years ago. You haven't seen the couple for years, but you hear they live in different states now.

   What could have happened since you last saw them?

   ____

4. You want to move to a smaller home. You won't be able to fit all your furniture into your new place.

   What can you do with the extra furniture?

   ____

Understanding & Applying Information

5. You want to buy a birthday present for your cousin. She's lost a lot of weight lately, so she needs new clothes. She usually wears casual pants and tops. You also know the colors she likes to wear.

   What other information do you need to have before you buy her a present?

   ____

   What could happen if you buy her clothes that don't fit her?

   ____

   If you're not comfortable buying clothes for her, how else could you help her get clothes that fit her?

   ____

6. Two families of your relatives live near you. Each family has asked you to spend Thanksgiving with them. You enjoy being with each family, but you don't want to have to visit both of them on the same day.

   What choices do you have for Thanksgiving Day?

   ____

   What other information would help you decide what to do for Thanksgiving?

   ____

7. You're rehashing a recent football game with some friends. You disagree about which player scored the winning touchdown.

   How could you settle this disagreement?

   ____

8. A neighbor's dog is allowed outdoors without a leash, and it often relieves itself in your yard. You've complained about it several times to the dog's owner, but nothing changes.

   What could you do to keep the dog out of your yard?

   ____

Understanding & Applying Information

1. You want to lower your blood pressure and improve the functioning of your heart and lungs. Of these suggestions, which make sense for you? Choose the correct answers.

   a. Do aerobic exercise at least three times a week.
   b. Walk two miles a day.
   c. Smoke exceedingly.
   d. Eat foods low in fat and cholesterol.
   e. Eliminate alcoholic beverages.
   f. Take medication.

2. You live alone and want to avoid accidents. What are some ways you can change your home so it is safer? Choose the suggestions that apply to you.

   a. Install a handrail on the stairway.
   b. Don't put non-skid mats under area rugs.
   c. Keep your driveway or sidewalks clear.
   d. Install and frequently check smoke and carbon monoxide detectors.
   e. Keep doors and windows unlocked.
   f. Keep drapes closed at night.
   g. Don't smoke in bed or lying on the couch.

3. You bend over to pick something up and feel a twinge in your back. When you stand up, it is painful.

   What might have happened? ____

   What should you do? ____

   What is the correct way to pick something up? ______________________________

4. It's hurricane season and a tropical storm is brewing. You live near the coast.

   How can you secure your belongings and prepare your family if the storm gets destructive?
   ____

   What information should you have? ________________________________

   What choices do you have? ____

Understanding & Applying Information

5. You want your neighborhood to be safe for the kids when they trick-or-treat. Many of your neighbors don't have kids at home anymore, but they are grandparents.

   What do you need to do to rally support for your idea?

   ____

   How could you involve the grandparents in your neighborhood?

   ____

   What kinds of activities can you arrange so the kids and your neighbors enjoy the evening?

   ____

6. You're going on a vacation with a tour group. The brochure suggests getting in shape for the hiking and walking you'll be doing on the tour.

   How will you prepare?

   ____

   What resources are available in your community to help you prepare?

   ____

   What information do you need to know from the tour group before you begin?

   ____

7. You started on a diet and want to lose ten pounds. Your doctor suggests you take vitamin supplements and gives you a list of ten to take throughout the day. You don't think you'll remember to take them at the times your doctor prescribed.

   What can you do?

   ____

   Who might be able to help you?

   ____

Understanding & Applying Information

1. You like to take adventure vacations. You and a friend have signed up for a hiking trip through the northern mountains of Costa Rica. Both of you know very little about the weather or the terrain.

   What might happen if you don't investigate the weather and terrain?

   a. You might get lost.

   b. You might not pack the right clothing or equipment.

   c. You might not have anywhere to stay.

   How do you investigate about a country you're to visit?

   a. Go to the library, use the Internet, or buy a travel book about the country.

   b. Don't study. Just assume that you know best.

   c. Don't worry. Your travel guide will tell you everything you need to know.

2. You are just beginning to understand the game of football. The referee calls one team *offside* and assesses them a penalty.

   What do you think *offside* might mean?

   a. A player runs onto the sidelines.

   b. A player moves forward at the line of scrimmage before a play is initiated.

   c. A player runs into the wrong end zone.

   What's the best thing to do when you don't know the meaning of a sports term?

   a. Ask someone who really knows the game.

   b. Call a sports commentator on your local TV station.

   c. Just watch and hope you'll figure it out eventually.

3. Jackie Joyner Kersey was an Olympic gold medalist in track who died of suffocation after experiencing a seizure while sleeping. She was 38 years old.

   What else would you like to know to understand her death better? Choose two answers.

   a. how her eating habits contributed to her death

   b. how she grew her fingernails to be six inches long

   c. what family history or drug regimen might have been factors in her death

Understanding & Applying Information

How would authorities be able to investigate her cause of death?

a. Do an autopsy.
b. Take a family health history from her father's and mother's families.
c. all of the above

4. You want to sign up for an aerobics course. You don't know if you should take a basic aerobics course, a step aerobics course, or a water aerobics course.

   What do you need to do to make the best decision? Choose two answers.

   a. Close your eyes and pick a name out of a hat.
   b. Talk to your physician about each one.
   c. Try each one and then decide.

   What other information do you need to gather to decide? Choose two answers.

   a. the aerobic difficulty of each class
   b. the type of clothing required for each class
   c. how well-dressed the other participants are

5. You think you and your spouse might enjoy taking an ocean liner cruise. Many of your friends have taken one, but they've all gone to different destinations.

   What do you need to find out to make a decision about your destination?

   a. the size of the boat, the name of the captain, and the cost per person
   b. the cost per person, the activities at the ports of call, and the length of the cruise
   c. the activities aboard the boat, the activities at the ports of call, and the cost and length of the cruise

   What do you need to find out to plan for the major costs of the trip?

   a. round trip airfare or mileage to and from the ship, cost of the cruise, and cost of activities in the ports of call
   b. what new clothes you'll need, the cost of drinks in port, and the cost of airport parking
   c. if your kids will give you the cruise for your anniversary

   What are some things you need to bring with you on an ocean liner cruise?

   ____________________ ____________________

   ____________________ ____________________

Understanding & Applying Information

6. You want to spend this beautiful autumn day outside. You enjoy being with people, getting some exercise, and doing a variety of activities.

   How should you plan your day to provide for all of the above considerations?

   a. Golf 36 holes of golf with your best friend.
   b. Go bowling first.
   c. Drive to a nearby nature preserve with some friends. Call ahead to go horseback riding, canoeing, and picnicking.

   What else would you like to know about the nature preserve?

   a. if the leaves are changing
   b. the cost of various activities and the entrance fee
   c. the names of the rangers

   What are some other outdoor activities you can do with people?

   a. Watch a football game.
   b. Play a game of bridge.
   c. Play horseshoes.

7. You just bought your grandson a new mountain bike. Now you can go biking together. He wears a helmet and wonders why you don't.

   What should you say?

   a. "Don't tell me what to do!"
   b. "Thanks for reminding me. We should both wear helmets if we're going to ride."
   c. "Only babies wear helmets. Are you still a baby?"

   You ride up behind some people on the bike path. They are taking up the whole path. What can you say to them?

   a. "Get out of our way!"
   b. "Excuse us, please, we're coming through."
   c. "We're going to tell the ranger if you don't move out of our way instantly."

   What are some safety concerns you should check for before you ride a bike?

   ____

   ____

   ____

Paraphrasing & Summarizing

Money

Work

Family & Social Relationships

Health & Safety

Sports & Leisure

Perhaps the most automatic skills our brain uses to solve problems are *paraphrasing* and *summarizing*. A person whose metacognitive problem-solving process doesn't include an automatic filter for restating problems and boiling them down to their salient, or obvious points is at a real disadvantage. As problem solvers, we need to automatically look at challenging, unfamiliar information and rearrange or restate it so our minds can process the facts in a familiar way.

Many people consider paraphrasing and summarizing to be synonyms. Although both skills allow us to process information in order for it to be more useful, there is a distinct difference. When we paraphrase, we use synonyms and words familiar to us to restate and simplify complicated sentences and difficult vocabulary. Summarizing allows us to reduce a large volume of information into its most important points. A daily to-do list is basically a summary of our activities for an entire day. If a boss asks you to summarize an important phone call you took from a client, it's imperative that you are able to relay the conversation to your boss clearly, correctly, and gracefully.

In this unit, you'll practice paraphrasing information in problems by choosing alternate vocabulary and restating sentences in your own words. These small steps are the kind of practice required to make paraphrasing skills an automatic metacognitive process.

You'll also practice summarizing by pulling only the most important information contained in a problem and ignoring factors that aren't related to a solution. As you become more skilled at summarizing information, you will find yourself solving problems quicker and with less confusion.

Paraphrasing & Summarizing

1. You receive a notice from the bank that says, "There are insufficient funds in your account to cover the checks you've written."

   What's another way to say that?

   a. Your checking account is in good shape.
   b. You don't have enough money in your checking account.
   c. You can go ahead and write checks.

   What word describes the status of your checking account?

   a. fortified
   b. withdrawn
   c. overdrawn

2. You are working on your budget because you're considering buying a new car. Currently, you pay $250 a month for your car. The car you're looking at would cost about $300 a month. You'll be able to afford it if you don't increase your spending on other things in your budget.

   What best summarizes this situation?

   a. You watch your budget carefully.
   b. You can't afford a new car.
   c. You can afford to buy a new car if you watch your budget carefully.

   What's another way to say, "Your car payment will increase $50 per month"?

   a. Your new car costs $50 more a month than your old car.
   b. Your new car costs about the same as your old car.
   c. Your new car payment is $50 a month.

3. You see the following sign at your bank:

   All noncustomers of First Bank will be required to pay a $3 service charge for each check cashed.

   What's another way to say that information?

   a. Anyone who cashes a check has to pay $3.
   b. There is no charge for check cashing.
   c. If you aren't a customer, you have to pay for check cashing.

Paraphrasing & Summarizing

4. You get a notice from the phone company that reads, "If we do not receive payment in full by May 13, your phone service will be disconnected."

   What's another way to say that?

   ____

   The second part of the notice reads, "If service is discontinued, you may incur additional fees for reconnection of service." What's another way to say that?

   ____

5. You have an insurance premium of $150 to pay on the 21st of next month. There is a penalty for making a late payment. You often forget about this bill.

   What's the important information you need to remember?

   ____

   ____

6. A friend wants some information about an investment. She asks you to call the bank for her. The person at the bank says, "We're having a special on Certificates of Deposit. The current rate is 5.9% for a three-month CD and 6% for a six-month CD."

   What would you say to relay this message to your friend?

   ____

   ____

7. You receive your credit card statement and notice something is wrong. There is a charge on your account for $200 to a music store. You know you didn't make this purchase and think someone else might be using your number. You don't think you should pay for this purchase. Pretend you're calling your credit card company and explain the situation to them.

   ____

   ____

   ____

   ____

   ____

Paraphrasing & Summarizing

1. Your boss says, "You're not the slowest worker in the department, but you're not exactly fast, either."

   What's a better way to say that?

   a. "Why are you so slow?"
   b. "What's the matter with you?"
   c. "I'd like you to work a little faster."

2. You like to keep your radio on while you're at your desk. A co-worker next to you says, "You think it's great to listen to that radio. What about the rest of us? You just don't care about anyone but yourself."

   What does your co-worker want you to do?

   a. Play a different radio station.
   b. Ask your co-workers' permission before you play your radio.
   c. Take your co-workers to lunch.

3. You receive the following memo from the owner of your company: "We've experienced a recent rise in sales, coupled with a decline in overall expenses. The net result has had a positive impact on our bottom line."

   What's the best restatement of this memo.

   a. Our sales are up and our expenses are down. We're making more profit.
   b. We're selling less and spending more. We need to make more profit.
   c. If we keep spending so much, this company will sink.

4. You accuse a friend of spending her money foolishly. Your friend replies, "I wouldn't talk if I were you."

   What does your friend mean?

   ___

   ___

   What's a more polite way to say, "Don't spend your money foolishly"?

   ___

   ___

Paraphrasing & Summarizing

5. A friend of yours is looking for a job as a receptionist. You see this want ad below.

> **RECEPTIONIST WANTED**
>
> Mailing company seeks take-charge, detail-oriented person. Must be articulate, have good grammar skills, and be able to handle a variety of tasks. Duties include main switchboard, data entry, and appointment scheduling. Must be computer literate. Competitive salary and benefits. Call Pat Kiyoto (900) 555-7177 or fax (615) 555-7178.

Summarize what you would say on the phone to tell your friend about this job opportunity.

____

____

____

6. Your boss tells you the following information during your performance review:

- You get along well with your co-workers.
- You are punctual.
- You are rarely sick or out of the office for personal reasons.
- Your errors have cost the company lots of money.
- You will have another performance review in one month.

Summarize what you would say to a good friend to summarize your performance review.

____

____

____

7. Matt, a young friend, asks your advice about choosing a career. He enjoys working with computers. He often modifies software programs to suit his needs. Many of his friends ask him to problem-solve troubles with their computer hardware and software. Matt is also an exceptional writer. He has excellent grammar skills, and he writes in a clear style that's easy to understand. No one gets lost when Matt writes the directions for going someplace!

What types of careers would you suggest to Matt?

______________________ ______________________

______________________ ______________________

Paraphrasing & Summarizing

1. Your friend says, "I don't have a free weekend for two months, and then it's holiday time."

   What could she mean?

   a. I don't have time to visit for at least four months.
   b. Let's get together for the holidays.
   c. I can't visit until after the holidays.
   d. Why don't you visit me?

2. Your son-in-law lost his job. Your daughter tearfully told you the story and she's not sure they'll be able to meet all of their financial obligations.

   What might your daughter really be saying?

   a. She's hoping you'll help her financially.
   b. She needs someone to understand and listen.
   c. She'd like to get your advice on how to handle their financial situation.
   d. all of the above

3. You hear a man's voice behind you say, "Down in front, bud. We can't see back here."

   Why is he saying this? ______________________________

   What is a better way for him to handle the situation? ______________________

4. You attend your first high school class reunion in 20 years. One of your classmates says, "I'd recognize you anywhere!"

   What does she mean by this? ______________________________

5. You've been invited to attend a political fund-raiser in the governor's mansion. It's a black-tie affair.

   What is a *black-tie affair*? ______________________________

6. You've been asked to bring dessert to a family dinner. Your family knows you'd rather cook than bake, so you're upset they asked you to bake something. You've mentioned your preference several times but nothing changes.

   What's another way to make your preference known?

   ____

Paraphrasing & Summarizing

7. Your son's science teacher speaks highly of your son's work. His teacher particularly likes the questions he asks in class and his willingness to discuss class topics.

   How will you summarize the conference to your son?

   ____

   ____

8. Your parents are recently retired. Your mom dove into hobbies and projects she's put off doing for years. She's busy every day and is often gone for the entire day. Your dad has a hobby, but it doesn't take him away from home very often. In fact, he's upset that your mom's away so much. He came to see you after he'd had a serious disagreement with your mom about her schedule.

   What is your dad's complaint?

   ____

   ____

9. You are recently divorced. Your friend insists on introducing you to her best friend and hopes you two will hit it off. You're not ready to make conversation with a stranger, much less get back into the dating scene. You're getting used to being single again and find you like that lifestyle very much. You know your friend means well so you don't want to hurt her feelings.

   How can you tell her about your decision?

   ____

   ____

10. Your brother has recently remarried. His grown children do not like his new wife. You sat with your nieces at the reception and calmly listened to their complaints. During the reception, one daughter criticized your brother's wife so that others could hear. Your brother and niece fought, and your mother got involved. Everyone became angry with you for leaving the scene.

    Write a sentence to summarize the incident at the reception.

    ____

    ____

Paraphrasing & Summarizing

1. Your physician says your cholesterol is too high.

   What does that mean?

   a. You weigh too much.
   b. You are diabetic.
   c. You are eating too much fat.

2. Your physician tells you to lower your fat intake to about 30 grams a day.

   What's another way of saying this?

   a. Read food labels to find out the saturated fat content and adjust your fat intake accordingly.
   b. Lose 30 pounds.
   c. Eat less sugar and more red meat.

3. You pass a sign on the highway that says, "Our state has zero tolerance for drunk drivers."

   What does that mean?

   a. "We don't like drunk drivers."
   b. "We'll give you a ticket for being drunk and driving."
   c. "We'll give you our stiffest penalty for drunk driving."

4. You have a small mole on your hand that has changed color and size recently. You go to your doctor who says she wants to do a biopsy to find out its status.

   What might *biopsy* mean?

   a. She'll put a patch over it to see if it changes color.
   b. She'll remove it to see if it is malignant.
   c. She'll put acid on it to make it go away.

   The biopsy report comes back and your physician leaves you this message: "The biopsy was negative." What does that message mean?

   a. "You have cancer."
   b. "The results are nonmalignant. Your biopsy did not show any cancer cells."
   c. "The results are inconclusive."

5. Fitness experts say that a 12-minute mile is better than a 14-minute mile or a 10-minute mile.

   What do they mean?

   a. Don't ride your bike too hard.
   b. Walk just one mile a day.
   c. A quick, steady walking pace is preferred over a too rigorous or too casual pace.

   Fitness experts also say that walking causes less hard impact than running. What does that mean?

   a. Walking isn't as good for you as running.
   b. Walking isn't as hard on your skeletal and muscle structures as running.
   c. Running and walking are just as easy on you as biking.

6. You receive a call from the fitness center regarding your membership. It has expired and you have a one-month grace period before you have to reapply and pay an extra start-up fee.

   What does this mean?

   a. You missed your deadline to pay your membership, and if you don't pay within a month, you'll have to pay more money.
   b. They want you to sign up again.
   c. You can't be a member anymore.

   What's important about this message?

   a. You used to be a fitness club member.
   b. You need to take a new class.
   c. You have a time line to meet before you're penalized.

7. You had your house tested for radon. The test came back positive.

   What does this mean?

   a. Your house has a radar detector.
   b. Your house contains a dangerous, odorless gas.
   c. Your house has been condemned.

   Why are these test results important?

   a. You will need to rid your house of radon in order to live in it safely.
   b. The city will give you a fine.
   c. No one will want to come to visit you because your house smells terrible.

Paraphrasing & Summarizing

1. You have a collection of limited edition porcelain figurines. You don't have one of the original choir boys, made in 1915, in your collection. Only 500 of these figurines were made, and now they are only available from antique dealers or secondary market dealers.

   What is a *limited edition*?

   ____

   What is an *antique dealer*?

   ____

   Summarize the above paragraph in one sentence.

   ____

   ____

2. You volunteer to tutor at your neighborhood elementary school. The principal tells the volunteers that information about the children who are considered slow learners "must not go beyond these doors."

   What does the principal mean by *slow learner*?

   ____

   What does the principal mean when he says, "must not go beyond these doors"?

   ____

3. You decide to go on a one day mystery bus trip to an unknown destination. You have to dress warmly and wear comfortable walking shoes. The package price is $25 , but lunch and snacks are on your own. You want to invite a friend to go on the trip.

   What does it mean that lunch and snacks are *on your own*?

   ____

   What do you say to your friend?

   ____

   ____

Paraphrasing & Summarizing

4. After your exercise class today, you went to your doctor for a volunteer screening for heart rate, blood pressure, temperature, etc. The nurse says you are as fit as a fiddle.

   What does she mean by *as fit as a fiddle*?

   ____

   ____

5. After your grandson's school musical, the people seated next to you enthusiastically say, "The show went off without a hitch!"

   What's another way to say that? Circle every logical answer.

   a. The performance was error-free.
   b. The group was well-rehearsed.
   c. The performance flowed smoothly together.
   d. The performance had its lapses.

6. The softball game took a long time to finish. It seemed like the players "moved slower than molasses in January."

   What does that mean?

   a. The players responded too quickly.
   b. The players didn't understand what to do.
   c. The players took their time.

7. Your friend calls to ask if you'd be interested in going to Ireland. The cost of the ten-day trip is $2300, round trip, double occupancy, taxes and tips not included.

   What are other ways to say *round trip* and *double occupancy*?

   round trip: ____

   double occupancy: ____

   What is *not* another way to say $2300?

   a. twenty three thousand dollars
   b. two thousand three hundred dollars
   c. twenty three hundred dollars

Paraphrasing & Summarizing

8. You are watching a baseball game on TV. The announcer says, "The bases are loaded; there's no more room to put anyone on base." Then a player gets a hit and the announcer says, "The batter hit a grand-slam home run—he's cleared the bases!"

   What does *bases are loaded* mean?

   ____

   ____

   What does *grand-slam home run* mean?

   ____

   ____

   The announcer then says, "They should have *pulled* that pitcher before he gave up that *dinger*." What do you think he means by these two words?

   pulled: ______________________________________

   dinger: ______________________________________

9. The local Boys and Girls Club is having a hobby day to introduce children to a variety of hobbies. They ask you to demonstrate and teach children paper making. The organizers want an interactive program so the children have something to take home.

   What does *interactive* mean in this context?

   ____

   ____

   Describe what your interactive paper-making program might be like.

   ____

   ____

   ____

   ____

   ____

   ____

5 Making Inferences

Money

Some problem-solving skills are more easily taught than others. For example, there are specific strategies one can use to paraphrase information or even analyze a problem. A skill like making inferences, however, isn't so easily approached. But an inference is often a key factor in how you will approach a problem. A correct inference can be a solution in itself. For example, consider that a friend of yours has been treating you very rudely lately. If you ignored the situation, it probably wouldn't get any better, but if you examined the situation closely, you could certainly make some inferences about why she might be mad.

Work

An inference is a *guess*, basically. Sometimes our guesses are correct; other times we're way off base. Many situation comedies base their whole plots on inferences gone wrong. The key to making inferences is not to jump into the deep end with an assumption. Dip your toe in the water instead and keep examining the problem until you've made the most educated guess possible. In the example above, you might jump to the conclusion that your friend is just a nasty person who enjoys being mad at you. But if you look closer, you'll probably infer a different reason for your friend's anger. Did you break a promise to her, borrow something and never return it, or say something behind her back? A good inference is based on a fact. The key is to find that fact and connect it with your inference.

Family & Social Relationships

A good inference is often based on more than just words. Other peoples' body language, gestures, or eye contact can help you make an inference as well. When you get dressed up for a special occasion and ask, "How do I look?" you'd better listen and watch carefully for your real answer.

Health & Safety

In this unit, you'll make inferences in a variety of situations. Consider all the factors available to make your best guess about what's going on.

Sports & Leisure

Making Inferences

1. A friend treats you to lunch at a nice restaurant. The atmosphere is pleasant and the waiter is friendly. Your food is served promptly and it's delicious. Your friend pays the bill with a credit card. The waiter looks unhappy as he reads the signed receipt.

   What might explain the waiter's expression?

   a. His shoes hurt.
   b. He can't read the signature on the receipt.
   c. He expected a bigger tip.

2. You're shopping for a leather purse as a gift for someone special. Some purses are on a table with a sign that says 50% off. You ask the salesperson, "How do these purses compare to the ones that aren't on sale?" She says, "These sale purses are okay, especially if you don't mind scratches or loose stitching. Most people don't notice."

   What does she mean? Choose two answers.

   a. The sale purses aren't as good as the others.
   b. You should buy a sale purse to save money.
   c. These purses are just as good as the others.

3. In a job interview, you ask about salary. The interviewer says, "Our salaries are competitive, considering our benefit package."

   What does that mean?

   a. We don't offer very many benefits, but our salaries are higher than other companies' salaries.
   b. Our employees compete with each other for salaries.
   c. We offer better benefits than other companies, but our salaries may be lower than other companies' salaries.

4. You see an ad for new pianos. It says, "90 days, no interest, no payments to qualified buyers. Call store for details."

   Can anyone buy one of these pianos on credit? ______________________________

   How do you know?

   ____

   ____

Making Inferences

5. You ordered a sweater from an old catalog. When you get the sweater, you notice the price for the sweater is less than you expected.

   What might be the reason?

   ____

   ____

6. Read this ad and answer the questions that follow.

   Mariel's Custom Framing

   Free estimates
   50% deposit required
   Call 555-9879

   Do you have to pay for an estimate? How can you tell?

   ____

   Why do you think the framers charge such a large deposit for their work?

   ____

   Does Mariel's Framing have only certain sizes of frames? How can you tell?

   ____

7. You offered to balance a friend's checkbook for her while she's in the hospital. You notice two deposits on her bank statement that aren't listed in her checkbook.

   What might have happened?

   ____

   What will you do if you notice that her account is overdrawn?

   ____

Making Inferences

1. Your co-worker's annual review is today. She's prepared a list of her accomplishments but she's worried she won't get a raise because one of her projects was over budget. Her review lasted about 45 minutes. When she came back to her desk she was smiling.

   What might explain her expression? Choose two answers.

   a. She got a positive review and a raise.
   b. She got a positive review.
   c. She was fired.

2. You showed your new design to your boss. You had worked on this for weeks and thought this was your best work ever. Your boss looked at the design and asked you to take it to the engineering department immediately. As you were leaving, you heard him call the engineering manager and tell him that an ingenious design was on its way.

   What did he think of your design?

   a. He thought it was wonderful.
   b. He wanted an engineer's opinion because he wasn't sure it would work.
   c. It was satisfactory.

3. You'd like to do some volunteer work for the Hospice Group in a neighboring community. You told your friend that you sent for information and an application. Your friend said you should volunteer closer to home and that your home community needs your talents with fund-raising events. You noticed her arms were folded across her chest.

   What message was she sending?

   ____

4. You hired a new assistant who will file confidential salary information. The man who was in that position moved to a different department. However, he'd like to continue filing the salary information rather than letting the new assistant assume the responsibility.

   What message is he sending?

   ____

   Do you think he is happy about the hiring of the new assistant?

   ____

Making Inferences

5. You eagerly accepted several additional responsibilities at work. Your boss said, "Thanks, you'll be handsomely rewarded."

   What does she mean?

   ____

6. You asked a co-worker to head up a new project. You believe she's capable. She responded by saying, "I feel like a square peg in a round hole."

   How does she feel about her ability to tackle the project?

   ____

7. The company your son works for seems very progressive. For example, there are no limits on how much vacation or sick leave an employee can take.

   What does *progressive* mean in this context?

   ____

8. Your pager goes off for the third time this evening. Your spouse says, "You're married to your work."

   What does your spouse mean?

   ____

9. You received a promotion recently. When the promotion was announced, a co-worker said, "Some people have all the luck."

   What is your co-worker implying?

   ____

10. You have the qualifications for a job you read about in the classified ads. The ad says, "qualified, serious inquiries only please." You have a great job but you're curious about this one.

    Given the information in the ad, should you apply?

    Yes _____ No _____

Making Inferences

1. Your mother-in-law invites you to lunch. During the lunch at a fancy restaurant, all she talks about is how concerned she is about her finances.

   What will your mother-in-law expect you to do when the waiter brings the bill?

   a. pay your half of the bill
   b. pay the whole bill
   c. pay the gratuity

   What do you think your mother-in-law really meant to communicate to you?

   a. that she would like some help financially
   b. that she likes to complain about money
   c. that she wants to sell her house and move to a different city

2. A person you sit next to at work keeps talking about how she'd like to celebrate her wedding anniversary, but she can't find anyone to baby-sit for her two children.

   Why do you think she keeps talking about this?

   a. She likes to talk about her kids.
   b. She wants to be your friend.
   c. She wants to find a baby-sitter.

   What do you think she really wants you to do?

   a. just sit and listen to her
   b. offer to baby-sit
   c. offer to find a baby-sitter

3. You've just finished a delicious dinner you and your spouse cooked together. You have several guests and they get up to help you in the kitchen. When you've finished, you all gather to relax. One guest says, "Gee, I really have a sweet tooth."

   What does this guest mean?

   a. She has a toothache.
   b. She likes sweets.
   c. Her dog is named Sweet Tooth.

   You haven't served dessert yet. What do you think this guest really means?

   a. She'd like some dessert.
   b. She saw dessert on the counter.
   c. She is offering to make some coffee.

Making Inferences

4. You have several friends who smoke. You'd like them to quit. You often send them articles about smoking or tell them about a documentary you watched, but you've never mentioned to them how much their smoking bothers you.

   What do your friends think about the articles you send and the conversations you have?

   a. You are a nice person with many interests.
   b. You are thinking about smoking, too.
   c. You are concerned about their smoking habit.

   What do you think your friends will do now?

   a. They probably won't do anything.
   b. They'll quit just because you want them to.
   c. They'll ask you if you want to start smoking.

5. You're getting dressed for a party. Your wife comes into the bedroom and says, "Are you wearing *that* to the party?"

   Why do you think your wife asked you that?

   a. She wants to dress in something that matches what you're wearing.
   b. She's not sure what you're wearing is appropriate.
   c. She likes what you're wearing.

   What do you think your wife would like you to do?

   a. pick something else to wear
   b. ask her opinion about what you should wear
   c. just wear what you already have on

6. "Pretzel sure is whining a lot," you say to your daughter as the dog stands at the door.

   What does your daughter think the comment about your dog probably means?

   a. Pretzel needs to go out.
   b. Pretzel is sad.
   c. Pretzel is a pest.

   What do you think your daughter might say next?

   a. "Hey, who's Pretzel?"
   b. "Get Pretzel."
   c. "I'll take Pretzel out."

Making Inferences

1. Your recent hearing test showed a moderate hearing loss in one ear and a less significant loss in the other ear. The audiologist said, "Two hearing aids are the preferred treatment, but one aid should help significantly. It's your choice."

   What does the audiologist mean?

   ____

   ____

2. You are 30 pounds overweight, and your doctor says you need to begin a diet and an exercise program right away. He gives you information and a phone number for the Excell Fitness and Rehab Center. He'll see you again in three months.

   What do you think your doctor expects will happen during the three months?

   ____

   ____

3. You have arthritis and it's difficult for you to move around, but your doctor feels you should exercise regularly. She says water exercises are less harmful for joints than walking or biking.

   What exercises will the doctor likely recommend for you?

   ____

   ____

4. Your friend is in the hospital trying to get her diabetes regulated. A sign on her door says, "Note to Visitors: Restricted Diet—No Food Allowed in Room."

   What is the reason for the sign?

   a. Harmful food could be brought in.

   b. Bringing in food makes more work for the hospital staff.

   c. The patient's food intake is being monitored.

Making Inferences

5. Read this advertisement and answer the questions that follow.

> **Harbor Crest Village**
>
> *Catered Living*
> *Personalized Service as Special as You Are*
>
> Catered living residents are provided with daily assistance in the areas of their lives where it's needed, such as meal preparation, monitoring medications, housekeeping, and physical therapy. Residents live in their own apartments on a floor with special amenities, including their own dining room and the security of a 24-hour emergency nursing response service. Call 555-2300 today for complete information.

Would you have to share an apartment? Yes _____ No _____

Does someone make sure you take your high blood pressure medicine? How do you know?

____

Are all meals prepared for you? How do you know?

____

What could you do if you become ill in the middle of the night?

____

6. After a recent fall, you begin physical therapy. The physical therapist recommends you rent a walker rather than buy one since your recovery is "like the speed of lightning."

What does that mean?

____

7. There is a blizzard in progress, and the owner of your apartment complex calls to see if you need anything. He says, "Don't venture out; you can't see your hand in front of your face!"

What does he mean?

____

____

Making Inferences

1. You're on the phone purchasing tickets for a concert. You're going to pick up the tickets at the box office. The customer service person tells you to make sure you bring a photo I.D. when you pick up the tickets.

   Why would you need to bring a photo I.D?

   a. to prove your age
   b. to prove you are the person who ordered the tickets
   c. to make sure you get good seats

2. You're planning a vacation at a resort hotel. The brochure says, "Check-in time is 3:00 p.m. No early check-ins. Check-out time is 11:00 a.m. Extra fee for late check-out."

   Why do you think you can't check in early?

   a. Most people don't want to check in until that time.
   b. The hotel never makes special arrangements.
   c. The rooms won't be cleaned and ready until that time.

   How do you know the hotel discourages people from checking out late?

   a. It charges an extra fee to discourage people.
   b. It doesn't practice good customer service.
   c. There is a law against it.

3. You see this sign on the golf course:

   No fivesomes allowed.
   Let faster players play through.

   Why don't you think fivesomes are allowed?

   a. Because four is a good, even number.
   b. A group of five plays too slowly and will hold up play.
   c. It's difficult for five players to get along well.

   What do you think would happen if slower players didn't let faster players play through?

   a. The slower players would get mad.
   b. The golf course would get ruined because too many people would be on it.
   c. Faster players would get mad because they'd have to wait.

Making Inferences

4. You've rented a video. There's a sticker on it that reads, "Be kind. Please rewind."

   What does this mean? Why would you need to do that?

   ____

   ____

5. You're playing cards with a partner against two other people. When your hands are dealt, your partner picks up his cards, smiles, and winks at you quickly.

   What could this gesture mean?

   ____

   ____

6. Your spouse collects antique postcards. One afternoon your spouse says, "I saw a beautiful set of cards in a store today but I just couldn't spend that much on myself, especially with Christmas coming up so soon."

   What do you think your spouse means by this?

   ____

   ____

7. You've decided to take piano lessons. At one lesson, you play a song that you've been practicing a lot. You think it sounds pretty good. When you finish, your teacher smiles and says, "This piece is really going to sound great once you've worked out the kinks."

   What does your teacher mean by that statement?

   ____

   ____

   What's another way the piano teacher could have said this?

   ____

   ____

Making Inferences

8. You're listening to a baseball game on the radio. The announcer says, "Rodriguez has been having a wonderful year with the bat. He's only hitting .215 with runners in scoring position, though. Let's see if he can improve on that average here in the seventh."

   What can you assume from the announcer's statement?

   ____

   ____

9. You go to the theater with a group of friends. You think the play was well-performed and you really enjoyed it. After the show, one of your friends says, "Well, there's two hours of my life I'll never get back."

   What can you infer from your friend's comments?

   ____

   ____

10. You're at a major league baseball game. As you take your seats near the field, you notice this sign:

    Fans in field-level boxes:

    Keep your eye on the ball!

    We are not responsible for accidents.

    What does this sign mean?

    ____

    ____

    What might happen if you ignore this sign?

    ____

    ____

Empathizing

Most of the problems we face every day can't be plotted on a flow chart or punched into a computer and solved based solely on the "facts." The majority of our problems involve lots of personal feelings—our own and those of the people we deal with. When we fail to consider the emotional implications of a problem, we usually fail to solve the problem successfully.

How many times (especially as a child when you had little control over a situation) have you felt you were being treated unfairly? When we impose blanket rules on people or situations, the outcome is usually viewed as unfair or at least incomplete by someone. Problem solving isn't necessarily about exerting your control over what's happening, but about your ability to create solutions that are appropriate for all involved.

Consider that you have two hard-to-get tickets to a concert by an extremely popular music group. You know at least half a dozen people who would give anything to go to the show. How do you decide who you will invite to accompany you? Whose feelings will be hurt by not being asked? Will you decide not to go at all and give the tickets to someone else? How will you decide who will get the tickets?

This problem is simple on the surface but it begins to become complicated when you start considering the emotions of everyone who might be involved in the solution. An empathetic problem solver considers both the logic of a solution and the emotional impact it will have on others as well as himself.

In this unit, you'll consider problems from an empathetic point of view. You'll practice examining your own feelings about situations and begin to factor the emotions of others into your problem analysis.

Money

Work

Family & Social Relationships

Health & Safety

Sports & Leisure

Empathizing

1. You've found a house for sale that you like. It's in your price range, is in a perfect location, and has been nicely cared for. You'd like to make an offer but you want more information about the house. The owner says he has two other families looking at the house tomorrow, and if one of them makes an offer, he'll take it and sell the house.

   What might help you make an objective decision? Choose the best answer.

   a. if the realtor would promise to get the information you need before the other families look at the house
   b. if no one else was looking at the house
   c. if you knew the owner personally

   How would that make you feel?

   ____

   ____

2. You have four grown grandchildren and would like to treat them to a weekend at a resort. Two of them are married and you can't afford to pay for their spouses.

   How might your grandchildren feel if you ask them to buy their spouses' portion of the cost?

   a. glad to be away from them
   b. insulted that you didn't pay for their spouses
   c. sad that you're paying for the trip

   How might the spouses feel if they are excluded?

   ____

   ____

3. You get $200 in cash at the ATM machine before renting a movie with your family at the local video store. The next morning you realize your wallet is missing.

   How do you feel?

   ____

   What might have happened?

   ____

Empathizing

4. Your daughter is paying her way through college. The last time she was home, she mentioned some things she'd like to have but can't afford.

   How would that make you feel?

   ____

   ____

5. Your spouse wants to donate $500 to a charity you don't like. Your spouse wants you to support this decision.

   How does his request make you feel?

   ____

   ____

6. You opened a checking account with the bank in your small town. You told them you wanted a checking account with no minimum balance and free checks. When you got the first statement, there was a $5.00 monthly charge for the no minimum balance feature.

   How does this make you feel? Why?

   ____

   ____

7. Your latest phone bill shows three long distance charges to numbers you don't recognize. You found out they were made by people staying at your house a couple of weekends ago.

   How do you feel?

   ____

   ____

8. You took your mom shopping. She found a necklace she liked and argued with the salesperson about the price. The store manager finally came over and asked your mom to leave the store.

   How does your mom feel?

   ____

Empathizing

1. You and a co-worker are job-sharing. Lately, you feel like you've been doing most of the work. You wonder why your co-worker is falling behind.

   What could you say to your co-worker to find out why her work is falling behind?

   a. "I'm concerned about you. Is everything okay?"
   b. "Keep up your end of the job or I'll report you."
   c. "Why are you leaving me all the work to do, you jerk?"

   Once you find out why your co-worker is falling behind, what could you say to help?

   a. "You should see a psychiatrist."
   b. "Let's get together and review what each of us should do."
   c. "You should quit this job if it's too much for you."

2. Your husband is self-employed. He works from your house running a lawn care business and a gutter cleaning service. During the winter months, he doesn't have much to do and he's always pestering you to keep him company. You have your own home-based telemarketing business that keeps you very busy.

   How do you think your husband feels about not working during the winter?

   a. He thinks it's okay.
   b. He likes all the free time.
   c. He gets bored and lonely.

   What could you do to help him think of things to keep busy?

   ____

   ____

   ____

3. You're working as a volunteer on the Holiday Parade. The executive director of the arts council is getting impatient and bossy with all the volunteers, causing them to talk of quitting before the project is complete.

   Why do you think the executive director is being bossy and impatient? Choose two answers.

   a. She doesn't like the volunteers.
   b. She wants everything to go perfectly.
   c. There may be things she's dealing with that you don't know about.

Empathizing

4. Your wife has been a stay-at-home mom for 15 years. She's been very busy transporting your ten children to their activities, volunteering in the community, and helping you to grow your career. Now that the children are all in school, she wants to go back to work at least part-time. You're not crazy about the idea because it will put an extra burden on you.

   Why do you think your wife wants to work outside the home?

   a. She wants to get away from all her parental responsibilities.
   b. She wants to fulfill another part of her life.
   c. She needs money because you don't give her enough.

   How does your wife probably feel about your concerns?

   ____

   ____

   ____

5. You've just hired a new receptionist to answer phones and greet visitors. He's been trained to screen all your visitors and phone calls. He deals well with the visitors but can't seem to direct unwanted calls to your voice mail. He sends them all through to your desk phone.

   Why do you think your receptionist is putting unwanted calls through to you?

   a. He has a hard time telling people you're busy when you're really not.
   b. He doesn't like to take orders from you.
   c. He doesn't know how to operate the switchboard yet.

   What could you say to your receptionist to help him understand how important it is to screen your phone calls?

   a. "Just do as I ask."
   b. "Let's talk about the types of calls I get and which people I need to talk to."
   c. "Put everyone on hold and hope they hang up."

   What could you say to your receptionist to solve the problem?

   a. "Go home and study the switchboard and don't come back until you've learned it."
   b. "Learn how to use the switchboard on your unpaid lunch hours."
   c. "I'll spend an hour with you this afternoon and show you how to use the switchboard."

Empathizing

1. Your grandson insists on bringing his dog along every time he comes to visit you. The dog sheds and you have to vacuum each time after they leave. This creates extra work and is a tiring task for you to finish.

   What will you say to your grandson when you ask him to leave his dog at home?

   ____

   ____

   How do you think he will feel when you ask him not to bring the dog along?

   ____

   ____

2. Your local PTA is having a luncheon and craft fair. One of your friends makes a negative comment about the dry-looking brownies on the dessert table. The woman who baked the brownies hears the comment.

   How does the woman who baked the brownies feel?

   ____

   ____

   What could your friend say to make her feel better?

   ____

   ____

3. Your granddaughter is home from her job in another state for a long weekend, but she doesn't stop by to see you. You tell your daughter you are hurt by this neglect.

   How does this make your daughter feel?

   ____

   ____

   What might your daughter say to make you feel better?

   ____

   ____

Empathizing

4. Your next-door neighbor, who has diabetes, fell and broke a bone in her foot. She's in skilled care and will be there for about six weeks because of an infection. This is the third time this has happened. The doctor says your neighbor should permanently move to a nursing home because she doesn't watch her diet or take care of herself properly.

   How do you think your neighbor feels?

   ___

   ___

   How do you think the doctor feels?

   ___

   ___

   How do you feel about this recommendation, knowing this is the third time this has happened?

   ___

   ___

5. You decide to give away some of your possessions as gifts. You ask one of your granddaughters what she would like to have from your china cupboard, and she says she doesn't want "any of that old stuff."

   How do you feel?

   ___

   ___

   What could your granddaughter have said that wouldn't seem so ungrateful and cutting?

   ___

   ___

   How will you respond to your granddaughter?

   ___

   ___

Empathizing

1. A good friend is coming over to visit. Your friend is a smoker, and you hate the smell of cigarette smoke.

   What is the best way to handle this situation without hurting your friend's feelings?

   a. Place "No Smoking" signs around your home.
   b. Just let your friend smoke and deal with the smell.
   c. Tell your friend how you feel and ask him to go outside to smoke.

2. You're visiting a friend in the hospital who just had a knee replacement. Your friend loves to play golf so you brought him a new putter as a gift. Your friend opens it and looks sad. He says, "Thank you, but I don't know if I'll ever get to use it. My doctor said I'll probably have to walk with a cane from now on."

   What could you say to repair this situation? Choose two answers.

   a. "Oh, forget what he said. You'll bounce right back."
   b. "I'm sorry if the gift made you feel bad. I just hope you'll get to use it soon."
   c. "Let me take that back and get you something more appropriate."

3. You and your spouse have been talking about spending more time together and improving your fitness. You're in a bad mood when your spouse mentions that he signed you both up for an exercise class. You say, "Have fun going by yourself. I don't have time for that." You see the look on your spouse's face and realize that this was a moment of excitement that you have deflated.

   Why do you think your spouse might have been excited about this news? Choose two answers.

   a. You are both out of shape and need to exercise.
   b. It was supposed to be a nice surprise for you.
   c. It would have been a chance to spend time together and get in shape.

   What might be a more appropriate response to your spouse's question, even if you still don't want to do it?

   a. "I'm not sure I'm ready for that. Tell me more about the program."
   b. "You know I don't like that kind of stuff. Let's just forget it."
   c. "It would have been nice if you had asked me first. I'm not going."

Empathizing

4. You're talking to your daughter on the phone. You haven't seen her for a while, but you know she's very busy with work and taking care of her family. She says with a sigh, "I just don't have the time to do the things I like anymore, and I feel so pressured into doing things I really don't want to do. I've been so stressed lately and I just don't feel like myself."

   What advice could you give her?

   ____

   ____

5. Your friend is very excited about her new grandson. She shows you some pictures of the baby. The baby is not very attractive. In fact, he is pretty odd-looking. Your friend says, "Isn't he just the cutest little thing? He looks just like my son, don't you think?"

   How would you respond to this question?

   ____

   ____

6. You've been sitting in the doctor's examination room for 45 minutes and you're getting very upset about the length of the wait. Finally, your doctor comes in with his head down. You say, "It's about time. I could have died in here." Your doctor looks up and says, "I'm sorry. I just had to give some very bad news to a good friend and patient of mine. It took a little longer that I'd thought." You feel terrible when you see the look on your doctor's face.

   What could you say to repair this situation?

   ____

   ____

7. Your son just bought a new house. He's very proud of it and asks you to come over and help him do some repairs. You walk in and find him on the top step of a stepladder replacing a lightbulb. Before even saying hello, you yell up, "Get off that top step; you're going to kill yourself!" You notice your son become very embarrassed and say, "Leave me alone. I'm not a kid anymore." Suddenly, there is a lot of tension in the air.

   How could you have handled this situation differently?

   ____

   ____

Empathizing

1. You play cards with the same group of friends every Thursday. Today you're playing a new game, and Gus is having trouble catching on to the rules. Everyone else catches on quickly. Gus throws down his cards and leaves the table.

   How do you think Gus feels?

   a. glad he doesn't have to play the game anymore
   b. hungry for snacks
   c. frustrated that he doesn't get the rules

   What might help Gus enjoy the evening again?

   a. Play a game he knows well.
   b. Introduce another new card game.
   c. Tell Gus not to be such a bad sport.

2. It's the bottom half of the ninth inning. Your favorite baseball team is at bat, and the score is tied. The first batter strikes out. The next batter hits the ball but he's out at first base.

   How do you feel?

   ____

   ____

   The next player hits a home run. How do you feel now?

   ____

   ____

3. Your friend brought his favorite CDs to a party. When the host plays the first one, a guest says, "Don't you have any decent CDs?"

   How does your friend feel?

   ____

   ____

   What's something that the guest could have said that would have been more polite?

   ____

   ____

Empathizing

4. A basketball player wins the Most Valuable Player award. He sends his coach a brand new car.

   How does the player feel about his coach?

   ____

   ____

   How do you think the coach feels when he gets the car?

   ____

   ____

5. You're watching the Winter Olympics on TV. The medalists for the men's slalom are standing at attention while the band plays the national anthem of the gold medalist. The silver medalist is crying.

   What do you think the silver medalist is thinking?

   ____

   ____

6. A neighbor says, "My in-laws are coming to visit next week. I'll have to listen to the same old stories they always tell, and nothing I do is ever good enough for them. They always say my food is either undercooked or overcooked."

   How does your neighbor feel about her in-laws?

   ____

   ____

   ____

   What's a way the neighbor could express her displeasure with her in-laws' constant complaining without causing any hard feelings?

   ____

   ____

   ____

Empathizing

7. You board an airplane for a trip. You locate your seat, but a man is already sitting in it, reading a book. You say, "Excuse me, I think you're sitting in my seat." The man grumbles, "Is that so?" and keeps reading his book.

   How do you feel?

   ____

   ____

   How do you think the other passenger feels?

   ____

   ____

   What could you do to make the other passenger happy?

   ____

   ____

8. You borrowed a friend's basketball to take to the park, but you forgot to bring it home with you. You call your friend to let her know.

   How do you feel?

   ____

   ____

   How does your friend feel?

   ____

   ____

   How could you repair this situation with your friend?

   ____

   ____

   Now how does your friend feel?

   ____

   ____

Evaluating

Money

Work

Family & Social Relationships

Health & Safety

Sports & Leisure

The ability to successfully evaluate possible solutions might be the highest-level problem-solving skill you can develop. It's also usually the last step in solving a problem. When we evaluate a solution, we weigh the pros and cons of each solution in front of us. As you evaluate, you ask yourself many questions:

- Which solution completely solves the problem?
- What are the drawbacks of this complete solution?
- What advantages does Solution A have over Solution B?
- What am I sacrificing by choosing Solution A?
- Who benefits most from Solution A? Does anyone suffer?

A big part of a successful evaluation is anticipation. Not only do you need to choose the best solution for the problem, but you have to look into the future and see how that solution will play out in the long run.

Imagine a friend's child runs his bicycle into your new car in the driveway and leaves a big scrape in the paint. One solution might be to demand that your friend pay for the repairs in full. What might that do to your friendship with the child's parent in the long run? But what if you always allowed this kid to ride his bike in your driveway and today you forgot to put your car in the garage? That might put a little different spin on the situation and require a different approach to the solution. A person who evaluates solutions and anticipates their implementation will be a more successful problem solver than someone who doesn't practice these skills.

In this unit, you'll weigh the value of solutions to a variety of problems. Pay close attention to the details of each problem and take notes if necessary. Remember to use some of the other skills you've practiced up to this point, especially summarizing and making inferences.

Evaluating

1. You're looking to buy a new house. You find one that's a bit small but within your budget. You find a second house that's just perfect for your needs but costs about 10% more than you are willing to pay.

   What should you think about in making the decision between the two homes?

   a. Don't worry about paying just 10% more. You'll enjoy the larger home.
   b. Think about what kind of swimming pool you'd like.
   c. Talk to your banker about a larger mortgage.

   Why might you buy the first house instead of the second?

   a. Paying 10% more than you had planned on affects other things you like to do.
   b. You think small is cute.
   c. The larger home was infested with termites.

2. Chicken breasts are on sale for 99¢ per pound if you buy them in a package of 12. You live alone and eat chicken about twice a week. Usually you just buy a package of three or four for $1.49 per pound. The sale price is a great deal, but you don't know what to do with all that chicken!

   If you buy the bag for 99¢ per pound, how can you figure out how much you'll save?

   a. Subtract 99¢ from $1.49 to get the savings per pound.
   b. Multiply the number of pounds you want by the sale price.
   c. Divide 99 into 149.

   If you buy the chicken on sale, what will you do to make sure that the pieces you're not ready to eat don't spoil? Choose two correct answers.

   a. Give the rest of the chicken away.
   b. Put the rest in the freezer.
   c. Let the rest sit on your counter.

3. Your 20-year-old son is a carpenter's apprentice. The car he bought when he was 18 has just died, and now he needs a reliable truck to use for work. He wants to buy a brand new truck, but you disagree. He can't get a car loan without an adult as a co-signer.

   What do you need to ask your son in order to feel comfortable about co-signing his car loan?

   a. "How much gas did your old car use?"
   b "Could you get to work without a car?"
   c. "How much can you afford to pay per month?"

What is a good reason you could give him to buy a used truck?

a. It costs less than a new one of the same model.
b. It has all of the "kinks" worked out.
c. It's better looking.

4. It's holiday time and your employer is sponsoring an "angel tree." Each employee picks a paper angel off the tree. Each piece of paper has the name of a disadvantaged youth and a present he wants. The time has almost come for the gifts to be ready, and there are still ten paper angels hanging on the tree.

   What will happen if no one claims the remaining angels?

   a. Those kids won't get any presents.
   b. Those kids will go to a big football game.
   c. Those kids will get presents from someone else.

   What could you do to convince the rest of your co-workers to take the remaining angels?

   a. Write them each a nasty E-mail about how selfish they are.
   b. Get the boss to make them take one.
   c. Help give them ideas about where to shop for the best prices.

5. Your daughter is a freshman in college and is complaining that she doesn't have a computer to use. You barely have enough money to pay her tuition, board, and transportation back home, let alone to buy her a new computer.

   What could you do to encourage your daughter to solve her problem?

   a. Find out if there's a computer lab on campus.
   b. Tell her to get a job to earn the money for a new computer.
   c. both of the above

   Your daughter says there's no computer lab at college, and she doesn't have time to get a job because of her studies and campus activities. What could you ask her to do so that she establishes her priorities?

   a. "What are the three most important things to you about going to college?"
   b. "Why can't you be more like your older sister?"
   c. "Do you want a computer or not?"

Evaluating

1. You are an electrician and considering a job change because you want to make more money.

   What things will you consider before you make your decision?

   ____

   ____

2. Your baby-sitter requested a $20 a month increase to take care of your daughter.

   How will you decide whether to keep this sitter or get a new one?

   ____

   ____

3. Your company is reorganizing, and you have a choice to make. You can stay in your current position or move to a different state and accept a promotion and pay increase of $7,500.

   What things must you consider as you make your decision?

   ____

   ____

4. Your customer service team was asked to make a recommendation on a new $75,000 automated phone system. You prefer people answering customer service calls — not an automated system. The new system would save at least $40,000 and allow your company to handle more calls.

   What are two pros and two cons of having the new service installed?

Pros	**Cons**
______________	______________
______________	______________

5. It's your birthday. Traditionally, anyone at your company who has a birthday brings treats in for everyone. However, many people are on diets.

   What will you consider as you plan your birthday treats?

   ____

Evaluating

6. Your company switched from three courier companies to two for delivery of packages to your customers.

   How will you evaluate the performance of each courier company?

   ____

   ____

7. Your company is expanding and adding a second shift. Second shift workers will work M-F, 4 p.m.-midnight, and receive $.50 extra per hour.

   What should a worker consider as he decides whether or not to switch to second shift?

   ____

   ____

8. Your company allows paternity leave. After using your sick leave, you may stay at home for an additional three weeks, but your pay will be only $150 per week.

   What things must you think about as you consider this option?

   ____

   ____

9. You want to quit your sales position at a department store and open a day care center in your home.

   What things must you think about as you make your decision?

   ____

   ____

10. You are a single parent with two grade-school-aged children. Your boss asks you to represent the company at a sales seminar at a resort a thousand miles away. It will last four days; you'll be gone six days with travel time. All expenses will be paid.

    What things will you consider as you make your decision?

    ____

    ____

Evaluating

1. You never know what kind of gift to give a certain friend. You take a chance on her birthday and give her a wild-looking sweater.

   How will you know if she really doesn't like the gift?

   a. She sends you a thank-you note.
   b. She never wears the sweater.
   c. She says, "Thank you. I never would have bought this for myself."

   What might be her expression if she likes the sweater?

   a. a beaming smile
   b. a confused grimace
   c. an angry scowl

2. Some friends of yours go on a long vacation and ask you to keep an eye on their house. You're over there one day and notice that newspapers are stacked up in the garage for recycling. You figure you'll help out by taking a load to the recycling center. When your friends return, they ask you if you know what happened to the back-issues of newspapers they'd been saving for their grandson.

   What should you have done differently?

   a. just ignored the newspapers
   b. waited until they got back and offered to take care of the newspapers for them
   c. cleaned their house for them

3. One of your children is having trouble learning to read. You talk to the teacher, and he suggests some ways to help your child at home. You begin working with your child and think things are going well.

   What's the best way to find out how well your child is doing?

   a. Wait and hope things get better.
   b. Ask your child if he or she thinks reading is getting easier.
   c. Ask for a weekly update from your child's teacher.

   What might be a sign that your help isn't working?

   a. Your child looks forward to working with you.
   b. Your child's teacher calls to tell you there has been little improvement.
   c. You are enjoying the time you and your child spend together.

Evaluating

4. Everyone in your family is very busy. No one seems to have time to do chores at home or keep the place clean. It's getting on your nerves, so you make up a job chart and assign each family member different tasks. You put the board on the refrigerator and tell them what they need to do. No one seems too excited about the idea, and no one follows through doing the chores.

   What might you have done differently?

   a. Tell everyone the situation and ask for suggestions.
   b. Just do all the work yourself.
   c. Ask someone else to be responsible for assigning the chores.

5. You surprise a group of friends by offering to take them out for lunch. You take them to your favorite Mexican restaurant. When you arrive, you overhear a couple of your friends talking about a bad experience they'd had at this restaurant.

   What might have been a better way to choose the restaurant?

   ____

   ____

6. Your spouse asks you what you'd like as a birthday gift. You mention that you've had your eye on a particular set of tools. When your birthday arrives, you open your gift. It's the tools you had mentioned, but a less expensive, lower-quality set than you had hoped for.

   What could you have done to make sure you got the set of tools you wanted?

   ____

   ____

7. You and a friend have decided to host a party. You want people to have a good time and dance at your party. There will be people of different ages there, and you want to choose music that a lot of people will enjoy.

   How will you make sure you choose music that will be popular with everyone?

   ____

   ____

Evaluating

1. You have a family history of high blood pressure and heart disease.

   What are some ways you can monitor your blood pressure and the condition of your heart?

   ____

2. Your doctor tells you to lose 30 pounds.

   How will you choose a healthy way to lose weight?

   ____

3. You have agreed to baby-sit a two-year-old for the weekend in your home.

   How will you make sure your home is safe for a toddler?

   ____

4. You have just begun a class for water exercising.

   How will you know if the instructor is doing a good job?

   ____

5. You're visiting a large city for the first time. You want to go out for the evening.

   How will you find out which areas are safe to walk around in at night?

   ____

6. You want to buy a leather couch.

   How will you know which couches are well-made?

   ____

7. You have been on a salt-free diet for three months.

   How will you know if the diet has been worth it?

   ____

Evaluating

8. There are two large grocery stores in your area. Your doctor has advised you to eat lots of fresh fruits and vegetables.

   How will you decide which grocery store is a better place for you to shop?

   ____

9. Your stockbroker gives you some brochures to review for pharmaceutical companies you might want to buy stock in.

   How will you decide which company or companies to invest in?

   ____

10. You are a judge in a low-fat baking contest.

    How will you decide how to rate the different desserts?

    ____

11. You're going to the mountains for a vacation. You plan to spend most of your time outdoors but you'd like the resort you choose to have an indoor swimming pool. You sent away for brochures from several resorts.

    How will you decide which is the best resort for your needs?

    ____

12. You live in an earthquake zone.

    How will you know if you've done enough to prepare for a major earthquake?

    ____

13. You've just begun a new, rigorous exercise program.

    How will you know how quickly to advance the difficulty level of the exercises?

    ____

Evaluating

1. You want to get more exercise by being on a sports team. Several team sports are available through the Parks and Recreation Department.

   How will you decide which sport or team is right for you?

   ____

   ____

   ____

2. You are buying a new camera to take on vacation.

   What criteria will you use for choosing a camera?

   ____

   ____

   ____

3. You're single again and would like to meet people your own age.

   What's the best way for you to meet new people?

   ____

   ____

   ____

4. You live in a rural area. Each fall you get several requests to hunt on your property. You are not anti-hunting but you are concerned about your personal safety since your home is in the middle of a heavily wooded area. You've posted "No Hunting or Trespassing" signs everywhere. When you came home yesterday, you found a broken window and an empty shotgun shell in your living room.

   What will you do next?

   ____

   ____

   ____

Evaluating

5. Your daughter wants you to enroll at the Senior Day Care Center. She believes you need to get out socially now that your spouse is deceased.

   What does your daughter think you're going through?

   ____

   ____

6. Emma's retirement party is next week, and you're in charge of organizing the celebration. Emma has worked for the company for a long time. After she leaves, you'll take over her responsibilities. Yesterday, you overheard Emma tell a co-worker she thinks you're pushing her out because you want her job.

   What does Emma think of you?

   ____

   ____

   What is Emma thinking about her retirement?

   ____

   ____

7. Your teenage son is on the Internet all the time. He's meeting people in chat rooms. You're concerned about these contacts because he's dropped all his regular activities and doesn't see his friends any longer.

   How can you decide if the Internet is influencing the changes in your son's behavior?

   ____

   ____

   How will you feel if your son spends a lot of time alone and doesn't see his friends much?

   ____

   ____

Evaluating

8. At your daughter's softball game last Saturday, a father of one of the other girls on your team yelled loudly at his daughter after she struck out. She walked slowly to the dugout with her head down.

   How did the girl who struck out feel when her father yelled at her in public?

   ____

   ____

   What was the father thinking while he was scolding his daughter?

   ____

   ____

   What would you have said to him?

   ____

   ____

9. Your older friend Gabby was jogging recently when she tore a tendon in her right ankle. Now she can't run for six months. When Gabby relayed this story to you and Agnes, Agnes said, "That's what you get for exercising too much. I told you something like this would happen if you lived too active of a lifestyle!"

   What does Agnes think about Gabby's exercising?

   ____

   ____

   ____

   What's another way Agnes could have conveyed the message that she was concerned about Gabby's health?

   ____

   ____

   ____

8 General Problem Solving

Money

Work

Family & Social Relationships

Health & Safety

Sports & Leisure

Up to this point, you've practiced problem-solving skills in isolation. That's a good way to work on building your skills to reach the next level. This section is that next level. On the following pages, you'll encounter many open-ended situations—many of them don't contain problems that are immediately evident. In those situations, you'll be asked to anticipate solutions to problems that might happen. In other cases, a problem will be very clear, and you'll need to answer several questions about its solution.

It's important to work on separate skills. A pitcher who is rehabilitating a bad arm makes it stronger by pitching simulated games. But eventually that pitcher will have to face batters in a real game.

This unit is meant to prepare you to face and solve problems in real life. Each pair of problems on the following pages includes a brief article, similar to those you might find in a local newspaper, and a picture that illustrates the situation. Use the information in the article, the picture, and your own experience to approach each situation. It might help to place yourself in each situation. Pretend you are experiencing the situation, and you might find that facing the problems will become that much easier.

A good problem solver uses several skills—analyzing, evaluating, empathizing, and the other skills you've practiced to create an integrated, holistic approach to problem solving. Use all the skills you have practiced, and those you already use, to tackle the problems ahead. Good luck!

General Problem Solving 1

Congratulations!

Grace enters contests and sweepstakes every chance she gets. Once in a while, she wins a prize or two. Last year, she won a digital camera and cashed in over 15 lottery tickets. Last week, Grace won her biggest prize ever—a check for $500,000 from Publisher's Treasure Chest.

Last Monday, an official from Publisher's Treasure Chest notified Grace by phone that she had won first prize in their campaign this year. At first, Grace thought it was just a prank call. But when the official explained the details about sending the check, Grace's heart skipped a few beats.

Three days later, Grace received the check in the mail. She and her husband, Phil, are overjoyed. She already has plans to use most of the money to help others. "We plan to use part of the money to help fund our grandchild's college expenses, but there are other people we'd like to help, too."

Both Grace and Phil are life-long community volunteers. They contribute their time and energies as hospital volunteers, tutors for at-risk readers, meal deliverers for Meals on Wheels, and organizers for local fund-raising events.

Questions

1. Think of some words that describe Grace. Write each word and explain why you think the word applies to her.

   Word: ____________________

   Reason: ____

   Word: ____________________

   Reason: ____

Word: ______________________

Reason: ____

2. Why do you think Publisher's Treasure Chest notified Grace by phone instead of in person?

____

____

3. How could Grace have checked to be sure the caller was telling the truth?

____

____

4. The article says that Grace's heart skipped a few beats when she heard about winning the money. Does that mean she should check with her doctor? Explain your answer.

   Yes _____ No _____ Why or why not? ______________________________

____

5. List some things Grace needs to think about now that she has received the check.

   ____________________ ____________________

   ____________________ ____________________

6. If you won $500,000, what would you do with the money? List two choices and tell why you would make those choices.

   a. ____

   b. ____

7. What did Grace mean by *prank call*?

____

General Problem Solving 2

Family Reunion

The Becker Family Reunion is held every five years, and this year Faye and Marv Becker will host the event at a park near their home.

They've made a lot of preparations for the reunion, including designing and mailing invitations to 60 relatives and planning a menu. Marv made arrangements with a local motel for special room rates for family members. They reserved the park pavilion and rented tables and chairs for the event. They have arranged all the details except for entertainment. Last Saturday, they got an idea for the entertainment when their daughter, Carolyn, stopped by with a large box of pictures.

Carolyn is interested in genealogy and is assembling a pictorial Becker family tree. She has collected hundreds of photos from members of the family and is preparing a written report of her findings with copies for everybody at the reunion. But Carolyn has several pictures she can't identify.

This gave Faye an idea for the entertainment. Each family will get a blank family tree form and will fill it out during the reunion. Families can work alone or together with other families to complete it. The most accurate family tree will get a prize. Prizes can be awarded to relatives who are able to identify the people in Carolyn's pictures, too!

Questions

1. The Becker reunion is held every five years. What can the Beckers do to make sure they have current addresses of those who will attend this year?

    ____

    ____

2. What arrangements would you make if you were organizing a large party like the Becker reunion? Check all that apply. The first one is done for you.

✔	find a location		design invitations
	prepare your house		pick music only you will like
	have a garage sale that day		prepare/cook food
	buy a new puppy		make hotel plans for guests
	call guests		include directions
	cook only spicy foods		plan a menu
	arrange for entertainment		plan to be out of town

3. How could the Beckers plan a menu to satisfy the tastes of most of the guests?

____

____

4. Faye's granddaughter helped Faye the last time she hosted the Becker reunion. This time, Faye's granddaughter thinks her cousins should do some of the work. How does Faye's granddaughter feel about doing the work for the reunion?

____

____

5. If you were planning a family reunion, what are some activities that would be fun and interesting for your family?

a. ____________________________

b. ____________________________

c. ____________________________

d. ____________________________

General Problem Solving 3

Does TV Run Your Life?

The average American adult now watches nearly six hours of TV a day. That means besides sleeping and working, most of our waking hours are spent watching TV, or having a TV on in the background.

Dave and Sheryl Maxwell felt they were watching too much TV. "It was always on," Sheryl said. "We'd flip it on as soon as we woke up and have it on in the background while we got ready for work. The minute I walked in the door at the end of the day, the TV came on. It stayed on until we went to sleep. TV was ruling our lives."

The Maxwells decided to make some changes in their habits. "There were four TVs in our apartment, and often they were all on. I boxed up three of them and stuck them in a closet," Dave said. "Then we decided we would only turn on the TV if something was on that we really wanted to see. That forced us to plan our TV watching time, rather than just having it on constantly."

So how does this couple spend its time now? "We've been playing a lot of music," Sheryl said, smiling. "And we've actually been having conversations with each other. When the TV was going in the background, we just had question and answer sessions. It's been nice."

Dave and Sheryl are in the second month of their experiment. They're still amazed at all the other things they've been doing since the TV isn't ruling their lives anymore.

Questions

1. Why did Dave and Sheryl decide to make a change in their lives?

   a. They wanted to reduce their electricity bill.
   b. They missed talking to one another.
   c. They felt they were watching too much TV.

2. What steps did Dave and Sheryl take to put their plan into action?

   a. ______________________________

   b. ______________________________

3. What does Sheryl mean when she says, "TV was ruling our lives"?

   ____

   ____

4. Why do you think people like to have the TV on in the background, even when they aren't watching it?

   ____

   ____

5. If you decided to only turn on your TV for special shows, which shows would you want to make sure you see?

   a. ____________________

   b. ____________________

   c. ____________________

6. What are some other things you think Sheryl and Dave do with their time now?

   a. ______________________________

   b. ______________________________

   c. ______________________________

7. Do you think Dave and Sheryl will stick with their experiment?

   Yes _____ No _____ Why or why not? ______________________________

   ____

General Problem Solving 4

The Proofreader's Problem

Elaine is a proofreader for a large daily newspaper. She's been at her job a long time. She's known as an excellent proofreader who is also very reliable. She has not missed a day of work in 31 years, and everything she proofreads is letter-perfect.

In the last five years, Elaine's newspaper has become totally automated. The writers and reporters now use computers to write their stories and create graphics. A problem has arisen, however, when Elaine goes to proofread. She refuses to use a computer and she demands that writers print their stories on paper and make copies for her to proofread. It has the other writers confused, and has her boss concerned.

Elaine's boss has spoken with her about learning to proofread on-line and has offered extensive computer training for her. But Elaine still insists that proofreading hard copy is the most reliable way to do it. She says she's been doing it this way for years without error and wonders why the company can't accommodate her style. She defends her methods by saying, "You can lead a horse to water, but you can't make it drink."

Questions

1. What is Elaine's major problem?
   a. She's been at the same job for 31 years.
   b. She doesn't want to do her job using a computer as her company expects.
   c. She's a stickler about grammar.

2. What could Elaine do about her problem?

   ____

   ____

3. What does Elaine mean by "You can lead a horse to water, but you can't make it drink"?

____

____

4. What might Elaine's boss tell her about her future with the newspaper?

____

____

5. If Elaine's boss says she'll have to start proofreading on-line or be fired, what is the best position for Elaine to take?
   a. Give up and quit.
   b. Take her boss to court for harassment.
   c. Set goals for herself to proofread on-line by a certain date.
   d. Ask for a different job at the newspaper.

6. The newspaper is a large company with many services available to help employees. Which of the following services might Elaine take advantage of to help her adjust to her new work demands? Check **yes** or **no**. The first one is done for you.

	Yes	No
Maternity advice		✔
Job counseling		
Adjusting to change		
How to invest your 401(k) funds		
Technology for Today		

7. If you were Elaine, how might you feel about your new job demands? What would you do?

____

____

General Problem Solving 5

A New Treatment

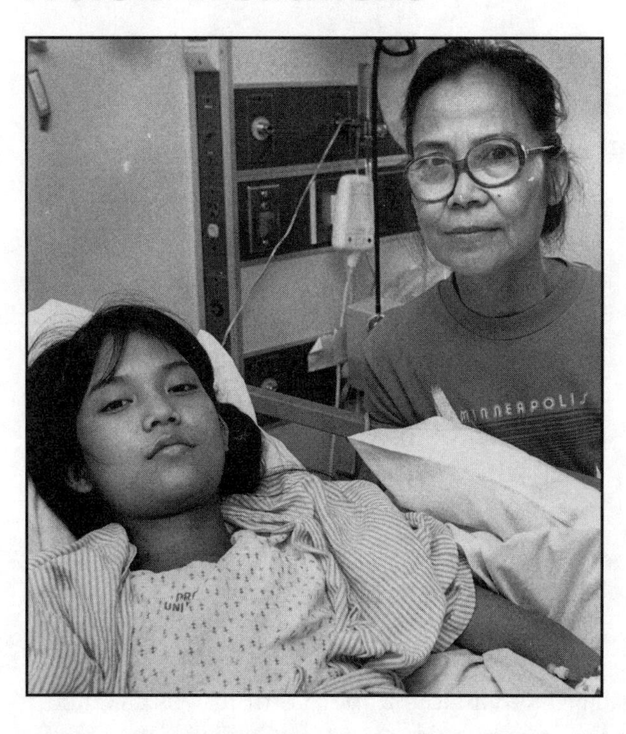

Lynn Lu hopes she will lead a long normal life after her treatment on Thursday. Until now, her thirteen years have been severely restricted because Lynn suffers from severe angina resulting from poor blood circulation to the heart. So far, she hasn't responded to traditional procedures and medicine.

But doctors want to try a new treatment. For this procedure, they will first use a laser to drill tiny holes into the walls of the heart's main pumping chamber. After they drill the tiny holes, doctors will then insert catheters which are easily pushed through the arteries into the heart. Doctors hope that this will relieve Lynn's crippling chest pain and help her begin to recover.

The experimental new technique is intended to help Lynn and others with heart disease so severe that it can't be corrected by traditional surgery. Based on preliminary studies by the Academy of Cardiology, the technique seems to be very safe and effective. No patients have died during the procedure. The Academy reports that two-thirds of patients treated appear to improve enough to resume normal lives.

Although there has been some skepticism about the procedure within the medical community, Lynn and her mother are game to try the new procedure. Lynn says, "I don't mind being a guinea pig. My quality of life isn't great now because of my heart and the pain in my chest. What have I got to lose?"

Questions

1. If you were in Lynn's position, would you opt for this procedure?

   Yes _____ No _____ Why or why not? ____

   ____

2. What does Lynn mean by, "I don't mind being a guinea pig"?

___

___

3. Put the following phrases into correct chronological order. The first one is done for you.

a. Catheters will be pushed through to Lynn's heart.	___
b Lynn will be prepped for surgery.	1
c. Doctors will insert catheters into Lynn's arteries.	___
d. Doctors will drill tiny holes to relieve the pressure.	___
e. Lynn will get to go home.	___

4. What do you think a *catheter* might be?

___

___

5. How do you think Lynn will feel right before the procedure?

___

___

6. Do you think alternative medical procedures or new treatments are a good idea, or should you always be suspicious of new treatments?

___

___

___

7. What does Lynn mean by, "What have I got to lose?"

___

___

General Problem Solving 6

Shopping Blues

It's four o'clock on a December afternoon, and the stores are filled with holiday shoppers looking for bargains. Wade and his wife, Ellen, have been shopping for three hours. Ellen is still full of energy, happily buying presents for their children and grandchildren. Wade, on the other hand, has had it! His back aches, his feet hurt, and he has a headache that won't quit.

Wade has been searching for a place to sit and rest for almost an hour. He has just found the right place. He found a nice, comfortable couch in the furniture section of a department store. Ordinarily, Wade might be self-conscious about sitting here and nodding off. Today, though, he's just grateful to have a place to take a load off his feet for a while.

Ellen was so busy shopping, she didn't even notice that Wade wasn't with her anymore. She bought a leather purse for their daughter and sweaters for their sons. Then she stopped at a candy display. When she turned to ask Wade's opinion about which candy to buy for a neighbor, Wade was nowhere in sight.

Questions

1. What is Ellen's biggest problem right now?
   a. She doesn't know which candy her neighbor would like.
   b. She can't carry any more packages.
   c. She doesn't know where Wade is.

2. What could Ellen do about the problem?

   ____

   ____

3. What do you think Ellen will say to Wade when she sees him?

____

____

4. Check each problem Wade is facing now. The first one is done for you.

   a. His feet hurt. ✔
   b. His head aches. ________
   c. His back aches. ________
   d. He wants to sit for a while. ________
   e. He doesn't know where his wife is. ________
   f. He's angry. ________
   g. He's embarrassed to sit on the couch. ________

5. What do you think Wade will say to Ellen when he sees her?

____

____

6. If Wade were more self-conscious, which behavior would he do?
   a. yell at his wife when she finally finds him
   b. squirt perfume at customers from sample bottles
   c. not sit on the couch

7. When you shop with someone else, what are some strategies to make sure each of you has a pleasant shopping experience?

   a. ____

   b. ____

   c. ____

   d. ____

General Problem Solving 7

The Scribe of Little Creek

Harvey has always been an avid reader and writer. As a boy, he read every book in the small library in Little Creek, South Dakota.

In junior high school, Harvey started keeping a journal. He recorded everything from the weather and current events to his hopes and dreams for the future. Everyone in Little Creek was in the journal, but no one knew Harvey was writing about them and their lives in Little Creek.

Harvey graduated from college and worked for a newspaper in Omaha until he retired in 1975. He married and had two children. All the while, Harvey kept in touch with the folks in Little Creek and kept adding stories, thoughts, and adventures to his journal. A few months after he retired, Harvey decided to start a lifelong dream. He used the stories from his journal to write a novel. He worked on the book for two years and submitted the manuscript to a publisher. It was accepted, and Harvey's book about life in rural South Dakota was on the bookshelves.

Shortly after the book was published, Harvey had a stroke and was moved to a nursing home near his boyhood home of Little Creek. Although he had some difficulty because of the stroke, he was able to read. His daughter brought a copy of his book to the nursing home, and Harvey read it to the residents. They looked forward to each chapter, and many of them added their own stories as Harvey read his book. For these residents and Harvey, the book became a wonderful book of memories.

Questions

1. What is a *journal*?

____

____

2. Some people in Little Creek were surprised Harvey published a novel about them. Why might they be surprised?

____

____

3. What might happen if someone from Little Creek doesn't like what Harvey wrote about them? What might Harvey have to do?

____

____

4. How would you feel if you were a character in a book that was written by someone you knew?

____

____

5. Why did Harvey's pals in the nursing home enjoy the book so much? Why might older folks like to reminisce?

____

____

6. Pretend you're writing a novel about people in your town. List four interesting people you know to be the characters in your novel.

   a. ____________________

   b. ____________________

   c. ____________________

   d. ____________________

General Problem Solving 8

Life on the Road

Some people might be envious of Diane Weiland. She spends nearly 40 weeks a year away from home, traveling all over the world. She's been in every state of the U.S.

Diane might be more excited about all her travels if she were doing it for fun. But for Diane, it's her job. "I work for an interesting company," Diane said. "We buy small businesses, build them up, and then sell them for a profit. My job is to research and visit companies we might want to purchase."

The variety of companies she's visited over the years is incredible. "Two years ago, I looked at a business in Kansas that made dental products for dogs," Diane laughed. "Just last week, I walked into a factory in the middle of the desert in Nevada. They make ice cube trays, believe it or not."

Diane says the work is interesting and she gets to meet a lot of people, but the job has its downside, too. "My husband and I are thinking about starting a family," she says. "And I don't want to try to raise a child while I'm traveling all over." Diane figures she'll do this job for another year or so. Then she'll try to find a position in the home office. What won't she miss about traveling? "That's a no-brainer," she said. "Waiting in airports."

Questions

1. Which statement is *not* true about Diane's feelings toward her work?
   a. She doesn't like waiting in airports.
   b. She likes the variety of companies she visits.
   c. Her job won't interfere with her ability to raise a family.
   d. She likes meeting new people.

2. Diane mentions two companies that she has visited. Which of the following products do these companies make? Choose two.
   a. ice sculptures
   b. dental products for dogs
   c. ice cube trays

3. How might Diane's work keep her from enjoying her family?

   ____

   ____

4. Diane wants a job in the home office before she begins a family. What are some other options she might have?
   a. ____________________
   b. ____________________
   c. ____________________
   d. ____________________

5. What ways do you think Diane uses to stay in touch with her husband when she's traveling?
   a. ____________________
   b. ____________________
   c. ____________________
   d. ____________________

6. What does it mean if something is a *no-brainer*?

   ____

   ____

General Problem Solving 9

Fashion Fanny

Frances Riordon, known to her friends as Fanny, is a costume designer and seamstress for the local theater. Fanny is a paraplegic who is confined to a wheelchair as a result of a car accident that happened when she was seventeen. This physical impairment hasn't stopped Fanny's entrepreneurship or creativity, though. Her business is thriving. Fanny's business is doing so well, in fact, that she needs to make a decision about expanding.

Currently, she works out of her small house, having turned the entire place (except for her bedroom and bath) into a production studio. She employs two other women who sew for her while she concentrates on design. The demand for her work has crossed the boundaries of theater.

Now, local women want her to design and make clothing for their career and entertainment wardrobes. Fanny would like to expand her business into this area while still keeping her theater business. To expand or not to expand—that is the question Fanny needs to answer.

Questions

1. What do you think is Fanny's biggest challenge in making the decision between expanding her business and keeping it the size it is now?

____

____

2. What is a *paraplegic*?

____

3. What things should Fanny consider when making the decision? Choose all answers that apply.
   a. the date of her birthday
   b. the cost of adding on to her home or buying another house
   c. the cost of paying additional employees
   d. whether she wants to supervise more people
   e. whether she wants to spend more time on operating the business and spending less time on actual design work
   f. whether her mother goes to Florida this winter

4. What are some good reasons *not* to grow a business?
   a. ____________________
   b. ____________________
   c. ____________________

5. If Fanny decides to buy a larger house, what will she need to consider doing to it to make it wheelchair accessible? Choose all answers that apply.
   a. Build a ramp to the door.
   b. Make the doorways wide enough to accommodate the wheelchair.
   c. Get new drapes for the windows.
   d. Make sure her bedroom and bath are on the first floor.
   e. Install an elevator.
   f. Provide enough parking for her employees and clients.
   g. Have two kitchens—one for her and one for her employees.

6. If you were Fanny, would you work from your home, or have a studio in a commercial area? Explain your answer.

____

____

____

____

General Problem Solving 10

Big Brother

The first thing Big Brother Jared Rock does with each of his Little Brothers is to go to the library. "A sharp mind can do anything," he says.

Jared is a Big Brother. This morning he's spending some time with his Little Brother, Marcus Pence. Marcus was already reading one book a week when the two were hooked up together in the Big Brother-Big Sister (BBBS) program—now Marcus is reading five or six books per week.

"We get two books on whatever subject he's studying at the moment," Jared said. "Right now, it's the rain forest. After he reads the books, we'll go to the library and local museums to look at objects, films, and other materials to make the material come alive." Right now, they're looking at the topography of a Brazilian rain forest.

The two spend three to four hours a week together. After the library, they usually go to Marcus' home to read and continue the mission of the BBBS program, which is "one-on-one friendship-building; the companionship between mature adults and children who need more adult influence in their lives."

Jared has been involved in the BBBS program for about 20 years. "I've been involved since I was an undergraduate in school. Marcus is my seventh Little Brother. I've always enjoyed young people. That's probably why I got involved in education," said Jared, who is a science teacher at Colton Jr. High. "It gives me as much gratification as anything I've ever done."

Questions

1. What is the purpose of the BBBS program?

____

____

2. Why is it important for a child to be able to confide in and trust an adult?

____

____

3. When Jared says "since I was an undergraduate in school," he means since:
   a. high school
   b. college
   c. graduate school

4. If you were a Big Brother or Big Sister, what are some activities you would do to help a young person?

   a. ____

   b. ____

   c. ____

   d. ____

   e. ____

5. Think of two adults that had a positive influence on you as you were growing up. Describe your relationships and how they influenced you.

   a. ____

   ____

   b. ____

   ____

6. What might happen to Marcus if Jared stops being his Big Brother?

____

____

General Problem Solving 11

Subway Adventure

Today is a big day for the Parker family. Ms. Parker and her three boys are visiting the big city for the day. They are going to see a children's musical in the city.

At breakfast this morning, Ms. Parker reminded her children of the schedule for their trip. She told them, "We'll leave the hotel at 10:00. We'll take a bus to the subway station, then catch the subway downtown. We'll get there at about 12:30, just in time to get some lunch before the show. The show starts at 2:30 and ends at about 4:00. We'll take the subway back to the bus, then take the bus back to the hotel."

Ms. Parker also reminded her children of a few safety tips to remember during their trip. For example, she told them to wear matching sweatshirts, so they could spot each other easily if they got separated. She also asked them to stay together, and she cautioned them not to accept food or candy from any stranger.

They left promptly at 10:00 and caught the bus to the subway. The boys had never ridden the subway before and they enjoyed buying their tickets and watching the stations as they sped by. Just as they got out at their subway stop, one of the boys, Mark, became sick and threw up. His forehead was hot and he looked pale. Ms. Parker thought about what to do next.

Questions

1. What do you think Ms. Parker asked Mark after he became sick?

____

____

2. What does Ms. Parker need to think about now that Mark is sick? Choose all appropriate answers.

    a. helping Mark feel comfortable
    b. what restaurant to go to for lunch
    c. whether to continue as planned or return home
    d. how the other children feel
    e. the subway schedule for a return trip
    f. cleaning up the mess Mark made
    g. taking Mark to the nearest hospital for surgery

3. Later, Ms. Parker told a neighbor about the trip to the city. Her neighbor said, "You should never have tried to take all three children by yourself." How did that make Ms. Parker feel?

    ____

    ____

4. What could the neighbor have said that would have supported Ms. Parker?

    ____

    ____

5. What are some other safety tips you need to consider if you're taking children to a big city?

    a. ____

    b. ____

    c. ____

6. Would you be comfortable taking care of three children on a short trip? Explain your answer.

    ____

    ____

    ____

General Problem Solving 12

A Special Valentine

Henry was in his early twenties when World War II began. He enlisted in the army and was stationed in Alaska. The work he did on the Alaskan Highway was hard, and the weather was wet and cold. Henry and many other young soldiers were away from home for the first time, and they were very homesick. Their morale was often as low as the temperature.

Henry's sergeant was concerned about the morale of the young men in his company. He noticed that nothing made his men happier than getting mail from home.

The sergeant knew if he could get mail to his soldiers every day, it would go a long way to boosting their morale. Then he thought of a solution. He recruited young women from all over the country to write to his men. The women wrote every day, and eventually, some exchanged pictures and phone numbers with the soldiers. Some made arrangements to meet when the soldiers were home on leave. The sergeant's plan worked. Morale was high among the soldiers even under the dreariest of conditions. The work was hard, but the letters the soldiers received helped keep them going and buoyed their spirits.

In this picture, Henry and his wife are reading one of the letters that Henry sent his pen pal friend during the war. The two are having such a warm laugh because the woman sitting next to him is his wife *and* his pen pal from the war. They're reading a letter that Henry sent to her on Valentine's Day 1947, a letter in which he asked her to marry him. Today is special for the couple because it's February 14, 1997—exactly 50 years after Henry proposed to his wife by mail.

Questions

1. What was the sergeant's dilemma and how did he solve it? Choose the best answer.
   a. Henry was lonely and homesick.
   b. The Alaskan Highway was in need of repair.
   c. His men just refused to fight.
   d. The sergeant required more hours of work than the men were willing to give.
   e. The sergeant was concerned about the morale of his men and initiated a pen pal program to boost their spirits.

2. What are some other ways that the sergeant could have boosted the morale of his men?

   ______________________ ______________________

   ______________________ ______________________

3. How would you describe the sergeant's personality? Do you think he was an effective sergeant? Why or why not?

   ____

   ____

   ____

4. Think back on a special Valentine's Day and describe the day as best you can.

   ____

   ____

   ____

   ____

   ____

   ____

General Problem Solving 13

The Book of Your Life

A new class is being offered for adults at Big River Community College next month. It's called "Your Book of Life: Creating Memory Volumes." The goal of the class is to allow students to organize photographs and mementos from their past into interesting scrapbooks.

Instructor Judy King (shown here on the left) says this class is a good opportunity for people to finally organize the boxes and boxes of photographs they have at home. "People come in here with a mess and walk out with a document of their own history," Judy said. "That's the exciting part of this class."

Creating a Memory Volume isn't just about cleaning up a mess, though. Students can take their books home to share with their families and friends. The people who benefit most from these classes are the younger generations who get to share this newfound history. Older students will find a whole new way to connect with younger family members once their books are completed.

Judy stresses that the contents of the Memory Volumes aren't restricted to just photographs. "Many students put diplomas, award certificates, even military medals and honors in their books. Some of the most interesting books have contained very personal items, such as favorite recipes and love letters."

If you've ever thought your past was boring or uneventful, this might be the class for you. You'll find there is much more worth remembering about your history than you could have ever imagined.

Questions

1. What is the goal of the class mentioned in the story? Choose all appropriate answers.
   a. to give older people something to do with their time
   b. to help older adults connect with younger family members
   c. to allow students to organize items from their past into scrapbooks

2. Why is this class aimed more toward older adults than teenagers?

   ____

   ____

3. This is an unusual class. What special qualifications do you think a teacher would need to teach this class?

   ____

   ____

4. Who are some people in your life you like to share stories of your past with?

   ______________ ______________

   ______________ ______________

5. What things in your life would you put in a "Memory Volume"?

   a. ______________________________
   b. ______________________________
   c. ______________________________
   d. ______________________________
   e. ______________________________
   f. ______________________________

General Problem Solving 14

A Business Venture

Murray Sanders and Yashi Yakamora are businessmen. They were recently on a flight together from New York to Los Angeles. The two men hadn't met each other until this occasion. They were sitting in the same row and struck up a conversation about tariffs.

It turns out they had a lot in common. Each man has two daughters. Each man studied at the same American University. And both Murray and Yashi love baseball. They're in different businesses, though. Murray owns a tire retreading company in Indiana, and Yashi owns a farm implement business in Tokyo.

By the end of the flight, they had decided something momentous. They decided to merge their companies. Now they're having a meeting in Los Angeles to make decisions about the merger and to decide how to approach shareholders about the deal. They need to consider the workers of both companies and how a merger might affect the workers' lives. They have many things to discuss before a decision to merge can be made.

Questions

1. What does it mean to *merge* two companies?

____

____

2. What could happen to the workers of both companies if the companies merge?

____

____

3. How do you think their two businesses can compliment one another? Circle all the answers that apply.

   a. The farm machine tires could be made from retreads.
   b. The employees could teach each other a new language.
   c. They could share resources such as personnel and purchased services.
   d. One business could help out the other in tight financial situations.
   e. They could travel together.

4. Suppose Murray and Yashi agree to merge their companies. What are all the ways they could conduct business? Circle all answers that apply.

   a. by phone, FAX, and E-mail
   b. One could relocate to their other's site.
   c. by carrier pigeon
   d. via mail
   e. person-to-person
   f. singing telegram

5. What are some of the reasons companies buy out other companies? Circle all the answers that apply.

   a. for an influx of capital
   b. to make work more fun
   c. to pool resources
   d. to downsize
   e. to acquire new products
   f. to become famous
   g. to gain market share
   h. to learn how to speak another language

General Problem Solving 15

Retirement Party

After 42 years, Sarah Plumbly will be absent from school. She's been in the classroom for 7,980 days. In all that time, she's been absent only five days. Her teaching career is finally coming to an end, and Sarah is celebrating with fellow teachers at a party in her honor.

Sarah spent her whole career teaching fourth grade. When she began her career, she taught everything: science, math, English, art, and music.

In her teaching, Sarah used slides, photos, and the computer to further enhance learning opportunities. But visual aides were hard to acquire in the early days of her career. Now technology is helping to make learning easier and quicker. "The context makes gaining information much easier for students," Sarah says.

Sarah is among an increasing number of educators who plan to retire from teaching in the next ten years. So many experienced staff members will be retiring that school administrators predict a hiring crisis as the pool of applicants dwindles and the number of vacancies increases. Sarah isn't sure the public is aware of the impending crisis in education. She is sorry to see the crisis happen.

Sarah looks back on her career with positive thoughts. "I ran a tight ship where everyone was expected to work and learn," she says. "I came to work each day loving my job and the children. I'm nervous about retiring and I'll miss the kids. I'm not sure what I'll do with my time!"

Questions

1. Based on the story, why do you think there will be a shortage of teachers in the near future? Choose all appropriate answers.
   a. The school district is laying off thousands of teachers soon.
   b. Fewer young people will become teachers.
   c. A lot of older teachers are retiring.
   d. Teachers are quitting at a higher rate these days.
   e. Students just don't like to learn as much as they did in the old days.

2. Why would visual aids have been difficult for Sarah to get early in her career?

____

____

3. What things could school boards and state governments do to ensure that more people pursue careers in education?

____

____

4. What do you think Sarah means by, "I ran a tight ship"?

____

____

5. What are your feelings about retiring from work? Will you be relieved or nervous about too much time on your hands? If you're retired already, how is it going?

____

____

____

____

General Problem Solving 16

The Big Sale

Decker's Department Store is known for high-quality merchandise and great customer service, but they rarely have sales. The store made less money than expected for most of this year, so Decker's decided to plan a special holiday sale to attract more customers during peak shopping hours.

The week before the sale, Decker's ran ads in all the local papers and on radio and television. All merchandise would be discounted from 10%-60%. Decker's hoped hundreds of customers would take advantage of their sale.

The night before the sale, employees worked late, marking down prices and arranging special sale displays. Everything was ready by the time the doors opened at 10:00 Saturday morning. There was just one hitch—Decker's didn't have enough salespeople to take care of all the customers.

This picture shows one of many lines of shoppers waiting for their turns to buy things. You might think all the waiting in line resulted in cranky customers. When we interviewed shoppers, though, not one was out of sorts about the experience. "With these great prices, I knew the store would be really busy," said one customer. "And people were mostly patient because they know that's just part of the deal when a good store offers great bargains."

All things considered, Decker's sale was a huge success. In fact, they plan to have a holiday sale every year from now on!

Questions

1. Which departments in the store were probably busy during the holiday sale?

_______________________ _______________________

_______________________ _______________________

2. Why do you think some shoppers help other shoppers, even though they're strangers?

3. Several shoppers offered these tips to make the most of a busy day during a good sale. Tell the reason behind each suggestion.

   a. Wear loose, comfortable shoes!

   b. Wear comfortable clothing.

   c. Be patient.

   d. Take a snack with you.

   e. Make good use of the time in line.

   f. Take time to drink liquids.

General Problem Solving 17

Lifting Spirits

Helen was 68 years old when she suffered a debilitating stroke that left her paralyzed on the right side. She and her family were devastated because her health had been wonderful, and the stroke was so unexpected. Once an outgoing, life-of-the-party woman, Helen became despondent and withdrawn.

Eugene spent his life doing what he loved—working. His first job was on the family farm where he and his wife raised three children. After his children took over the farm, Eugene worked in a grain research facility. When he retired, he refurbished the city park and maintained the green space in the town's small downtown. Last year a heart attack left him unable to do what he loved. Even his grandchildren couldn't cheer him up.

Sybil's health had always been fragile, but she didn't let that stop her. She was a hairdresser, choir director, guitar teacher, and chef. She shared her talents with anyone who wanted them, regardless of their ability to pay. Her house was filled with homemade crafts traded for haircuts, lessons, and meals. Six months ago she broke her hip and needed physical therapy. Friends said her eyes lost their sparkle.

Brooke Horvath was new in town and looking for ways to spend her free time. She heard about these special people who were now in the local assisted living home. She was impressed with their accomplishments and concerned about their spirits. Brooke found a way to help them regain strength and vitality. She volunteered to run a wellness program at the home, and she used the talents of these three special people in the program.

Helen became the organizer and scheduled exercise room space. Eugene brought the plants in the exercise area back to life. Sybil selected the music and planned the refreshments. In 12 months, their health had improved and their spirits soared. Sybil played guitar for evening sing-alongs. Best of all, when Brooke moved away, these three kept the program going.

Questions

1. What similarities do you notice between Helen, Eugene, and Sybil?

2. What problem did each one of them share after they had serious health problems?

3. What one thing did Brooke understand about these people, and why did her solution work?

4. Each person in the story made unique contributions in their lives. What interesting things did they do before they suffered serious health problems? What contribution did each make to the wellness group after his or her health problems occurred?

Helen

before:

after:

Eugene

before:

after:

Sybil

before:

after:

General Problem Solving 18

Sound Body, Sound Mind

Six months ago, Kara didn't leave her house for days at a time. She stopped talking to friends and family, and basically disappeared. Her husband had died very suddenly, leaving her alone for the first time in her young life. She became deeply depressed.

"I'd just sit at my kitchen table, drink coffee, and cry," Kara said. "Most of the time I didn't even know what day it was." Kara speaks these difficult words while taking a break from a strenuous tennis match with a friend. "One day my sister called out of the blue," Kara said, "and invited me out for lunch." Instead of going to lunch, Kara's sister took her to see a counselor who specialized in grief recovery.

"I was angry at first," Kara said, "but I knew I needed some help. Dr. Wilkins was the right person at the right time for me." Dr. Gina Wilkins has had incredible success bringing her clients out of their grief depression by prescribing a mixture of individual therapy, group encounters, and most importantly, vigorous physical activity.

"We're not exactly sure why it works," Dr. Wilkins said, "but we can't deny the success. Over 78% of my clients who have tried this program have reported a huge change in their state of mind. Most of those people aren't even supplementing their therapy and exercise with medication."

Wilkins says that there is a proven link between physical and mental fitness. "When we work out, our brains pump lots of 'happy' chemicals through our bodies," she says. "Apparently these chemicals are very potent in overcoming depression and grief." Kara's point of view isn't quite so scientific. "Hey, if it works, I won't rock the boat and ask why," she said, returning to her tennis match.

Questions

1. Which of these is not a component of Dr. Wilkins' grief recovery program?
   a. field trips to museums
   b. individual therapy
   c. vigorous exercise
   d. group encounters

2. Kara's grief was the result of her husband's sudden death. What are some other events that might cause people intense grief or severe depression?

   ________________________________ ________________________________

   ________________________________ ________________________________

3. Is Dr. Wilkins' approach to grief recovery a "sure thing"? How do you know?

   Yes _____ No _____ Why or why not? ____

   ____

4. This story illustrates a good example of an instance when it might be all right to lie to someone. What was the lie in this story? Can you think of a situation when it might be all right for you to lie to someone?

   ____

   ____

   ____

   ____

5. What does it mean to *rock the boat*?

   ____

   ____

General Problem Solving 19

The Farm Is in Good Hands

Lee Shur and his wife, Sandy, own and operate one of the largest dairy farms in Wisconsin. The farm has been in Lee's family for generations. Lee's grandfather bought the land and built the family home. In his whole life, he never took a vacation.

Then Lee's father expanded the farm by adding land to the dairy operation. Like his father, Lee's dad worked every day and only left the farm to buy and sell cattle. Lee remembers his friends' vacations and how thrilled he was to get postcards from them. Those postcards helped to form Lee's attitude about work. He vowed to take vacations when he ran the farm, and his attitude caused quite a stir in the Shur household.

Lee became a master of efficiency and added computer technology that significantly improved production. Although his father was skeptical, Lee outsourced some work, eliminated work that was redundant, and got competitive pricing from new suppliers. He kept his promise about vacations, too. When the crops were planted, Lee and his family took a vacation, leaving the farm in the capable hands of his workers. Lee's dad remained skeptical and stopped by the farm every day Lee was gone. But by the end of Lee's first year, his dad was his biggest cheerleader. Lee's efforts paid off in record profits!

Now Lee and Sandy spend their retirement in Florida while their daughter Karen runs the farm back in Wisconsin. Lee visits and is a constant source of ideas and advice to Karen but he doesn't look over her shoulder like his dad looked over his. Karen has made improvements and expanded the operation, and Lee knows she'll do fine. Best of all, he enjoys Karen and her family when they visit on vacation!

Questions

1. How did Lee's family change over time?

2. Do you think Lee's dad had a problem with his father? If so how?

3. What do you think Lee's biggest complaint with his dad was?

4. How would you describe Lee's father's and grandfather's attitudes about vacations?

   Lee's father:

   Lee's grandfather:

5. Is it difficult working in a family business? List some advantages and disadvantages.

Advantages	**Disadvantages**

Daily Bread

Under a new program at Central High School, students are being given the opportunity to earn classroom credit and serve their community at the same time. This program, called Daily Bread, is a joint effort between the high school and a local senior citizens center that is designed to benefit both groups.

Helen O'Connor is the food service director at the Senior Center. Under her guidance, students enrolled in the class gain experience planning, preparing, and serving meals for 130 seniors. Helen helps the students plan menus, decide how much food to prepare each day, and determine costs and any dietary restrictions residents at the center may have.

Helen also supervises the food preparation which focuses on one type of food at a time. This allows the students to try a variety of recipes within each food type, from salads to vegetables to main courses, and finally, desserts.

Helen has high praise for the innovative program because it's a great hands-on learning opportunity for her students. "The students have developed a positive attitude toward the project as they've gained experience and confidence," Helen says. "But that's not all. Having young people interacting with the residents on a daily basis has put smiles on a lot of faces at the center. I hope the program can continue for many years to come."

Darcy Drennan, a student in the class, agrees. "This class has been a great experience! It's just like the real world. You have obligations to meet. People are counting on you to make quality food—and you have to do it on time and under budget. Plus, it's one way to get to know the seniors in our community and help them out."

Questions

1. According to the story, which of the following procedures do the students perform? Choose all answers that apply.
   a. planning meals
   b. serving meals
   c. growing the produce
   d. deciding how much food to prepare
   e. writing cookbooks
   f. cooking meals

2. What diet considerations might the students make as they plan the desserts to serve for a week?

   ______________________ ______________________

   ______________________ ______________________

3. Why is it important for young people and seniors to work together?

   ____

   ____

   ____

   ____

4. List some ways both students and seniors benefit from this class.

Students	**Seniors**
______________________	______________________
______________________	______________________
______________________	______________________

General Problem Solving 21

Camera Problems

Sid and Nancy Quinn are from Raleigh, North Carolina. They are attending a family reunion in Napa, California, in two days. Since they live on the east coast, they don't get to see their relatives on the west coast very often. They had hoped to take a lot of photos at the reunion and on their trip to California.

The Quinns are also planning a side trip to San Francisco before they join the reunion in Napa. They want to spend a couple of days in San Francisco, take a day trip to the wine country just to the north, and then go to the reunion in nearby Napa. They bought an expensive, new camera before they left to capture the trip on film.

The camera seemed to work fine for the first roll of film they took in San Francisco, but now there's something wrong with it. They brought it to this camera store to get some advice. They'd like to get the camera working before they leave for the wine tour tomorrow. The salesclerk doesn't know what's wrong with the Quinn's camera, but she says they can leave it here for the night. She'll call them at the hotel tomorrow with the news about the camera.

Questions

1. What is the Quinn's problem?

____

____

____

2. How could they make sure they'll get photos from the reunion? List at least two choices they could make.

   a. ______________________________

   b. ______________________________

3. Why can't the Quinns just buy postcards of Napa instead of taking pictures at the reunion?

   ____

   ____

4. Suppose the camera shop can't fix the Quinn's camera. What could they do with the camera when they get home?

   ____

   ____

5. Many things like cameras or appliances come with a guarantee. How do you make sure you'll be able to replace a guaranteed item if it doesn't work?

   ____

   ____

   ____

   ____

6. What situation would a product guarantee for a camera cover?
   a. You throw the camera and break it because the shutter won't open.
   b. The camera slips from your hands and breaks on the concrete.
   c. The shutter won't open the first time you try to use the camera.

7. According to the story, the Quinn's camera was *not* broken by them. Check one.

   True _____ False _____

General Problem Solving 22

Gone Fishing

"You're never too old to fish." That's the motto of Holly Stan's off-shore fishing business near Tampa, Florida. Holly moved to Florida after she and her husband retired from military service ten years ago. They were the outdoor type, and Florida's warm weather gave them lots of opportunities to be outside. They were avid golfers, hikers, and swimmers.

One day they decided to go off-shore fishing with a local charter boat company. The experience was exhilarating and Holly was "hooked." She liked off-shore fishing so much, she asked friends if they'd go with her. Holly was surprised to hear that her friends were reluctant to go on a charter because of their physical limitations. Some used canes and walkers. Another had high blood pressure. Another had to take medication with food every few hours. These folks thought the ride would be too rough or, if they needed help, no one on board would be able to help them.

That was the beginning of Holly's Senior-Safe Fishing Cruises. Holly worked with several professionals in the area to lease and equip a boat especially for seniors. The craft would accommodate the special needs of most seniors, plus have equipment and personnel on board for any emergency. Holly went to work finding professionals willing to donate their time in exchange for a fun experience. She was enthusiastic and relentless.

Her efforts paid off. Within seven months, Holly had recruited a charter boat and a captain who knew the best fishing spots. A retired physician heard about Holly's idea and volunteered her time, as did two former emergency room nurses. She even got medical supply companies to donate equipment.

The first cruise went well. Everyone did their part and Holly's boat carried 12 seniors on the fishing cruise of their lives. The response from her guests was overwhelming. They all wanted to go again and suggested the next time they end the day with a fish fry.

Questions

1. What problem in her town did Holly identify?

2. What steps did she take to fix the problem and create a unique experience for her friends?

3. What precautions would you suggest Holly take for future cruises?

   a.

   b.

   c.

   d.

4. What does the name of Holly's company tell you about her primary market?

5. Should more companies make provisions to meet the medical needs of their customers? Why?

General Problem Solving 23

Safety First

These days, more people than ever enjoy outdoor sports. Crowds of kids and adults are taking to the streets on bicycles and in-line skates. Safety is often the last thing on their minds.

Who could blame people for not thinking safety first? By the time you put on knee and elbow pads, hip and wrist guards, and a helmet, you don't look much like the outdoors type. You look more like a medieval knight in shining armor than a skater or bicyclist.

Is all this safety equipment necessary? Some people say that all the pads and guards actually cause problems. They say shin guards and elbow pads restrict your movement. Others, of course, don't agree. There is one thing both sides agree on, though—a helmet is always a requirement.

If you don't want to strap on all the safety equipment, at least pop a helmet on your head. Most serious sporting injuries are head injuries, and a properly fitted helmet can reduce that risk.

The American Medical Association agrees with the importance of helmets. Ask your doctor, and he will certainly tell you that both children and adults need to wear helmets to prevent head injuries.

Questions

1. Which activity doesn't the article mention?
   a. skateboarding
   b. in-line skating
   c. bicycling

2. Why might someone *not* wear safety equipment when participating in these sports?

____

____

3. How would you convince someone to wear a helmet while bicycling or skating? What reasons would you give this person?

   a. ______________________________

   b. ______________________________

4. Why would the author mention that a "properly fitted" helmet would reduce the risk of head injuries? Why wouldn't you get the same protection from a helmet that didn't fit properly?

____

____

5. Can you name some other sports where you should wear a helmet?

______________ ______________

______________ ______________

6. What does a *knight in shining armor* usually mean? Is it used that way in this story?

____

____

____

7. Besides a helmet, what piece of safety equipment do you think is most important to wear when biking or in-line skating? Why do you think so?

____

____

General Problem Solving 24

Following her Dream

Being the oldest person in your class takes on a new meaning when you're 82 years old! Emma Youngster is a fourth-year senior at Mount Everest College in Lowlands, New York. Emma's lifelong dream was to earn a Bachelor of Arts degree and she's determined to make it, despite her failing health.

While working as a U.S. mail clerk, Emma envied the people who received college catalogs in the mail and she vowed that one day she would receive college catalogs, too. For years, she dreamed of selecting the right college, picking a major, and choosing interesting classes from the catalogs.

Things didn't quite turn out exactly as Emma planned, however. Her health began to deteriorate shortly after she retired. But two years later, with her health problems stabilized, she enrolled at Mount Everest, a ten-minute drive from her house. She wasn't able to take a full load so she took one or two classes a semester. She had to skip several semesters when health problems made it impossible to attend class. Over the next 15 years, Emma took enough classes to earn a Bachelor of Arts degree. She graduates this spring.

Emma's become a motivational speaker, too. She's often asked to be a guest speaker at senior citizens' meetings in Lowlands. She reminds her audience that it's never too late to accomplish a goal. She also shares her personal experiences with young people. She encourages them to set goals and begin working on them right away.

Questions

1. How many years did it take for Emma to get her degree? ______________________________

2. What motivated Emma to go to college?
   a. money
   b. pressure from her kids
   c. a lifelong dream

3. What was Emma's job prior to getting her college degree?
   a. mail clerk
   b. teacher
   c. motivational speaker

4. Would Emma's life have been different if she had completed her degree earlier? How?

   ____

   ____

5. List five things that Emma might say to a group of senior citizens in her role as a motivational speaker.
   a. ____
   b. ____
   c. ____
   d. ____
   e. ____

6. How might this advice be different from the advice she would give to high school students?

   ____

   ____

   ____

   ____

General Problem Solving 25

The Golden Oldies

What do you get when you put five lively, retired music teachers together? You get a group of music lovers who love to perform! They call themselves the Golden Oldies and that's what they perform—songs from the 1950's and before, including jazz and blues.

The Golden Oldies all live at the Galena House, a retirement village with a community room.

Fortunately, there's a piano in the community room, so they gather almost every day to practice and perform for the other residents. There's almost always an audience making requests, applauding, and cheering the Golden Oldies to do yet another number. The group has gotten such a warm reception from friends and neighbors, that other groups from the community are calling to schedule performances.

So far, the Golden Oldies have performed 11 times. While performing, they don snappy red vests, white shirts, and black ties to give themselves a professional look. The average age of the group is 72. But it's the sound that makes the crowd beg for more. Mature, trained voices blending in harmony, big smiles, and synchronized moves make a great act. Says one member of the group, "We love music, we love performing, and we love to make people happy!"

Questions

1. Why is the Golden Oldies a good name for this singing group?

____

____

2. What types of music do the Golden Oldies sing? Choose all appropriate answers.
   a. blues
   b. rock
   c. opera
   d. jazz
   e. barbershop tunes
   f. new age

3. Why is this kind of activity good for the performers?

____

____

4. What could a choreographer do for this group?

____

____

5. Do you think the Golden Oldies could plan a tour of other retirement villages? Would the tour be successful?

____

____

6. Which of the following is true of the Golden Oldies?
   a. They wear black vests, white shirts, and red ties.
   b. They wear red vests, white shirts, and black ties.
   c. They wear red vests, black shirts, and blue ties.

7. If you had the chance, what songs would you request the Golden Oldies to sing?

____________________ ____________________

____________________ ____________________

General Problem Solving 26

Jerome's Schedule

Jerome's aunt lives by herself and she has some health problems. It's difficult for her to see well, and she gets easily confused. Her apartment manager checks in on her every day, and one of her neighbors comes in to fix her meals and do some light housekeeping for her. Every other Thursday, Jerome travels across town to take his aunt to the hospital for her outpatient treatment. He doesn't have a car, so they have to travel by city bus.

Here's the schedule they follow: every other Thursday, Jerome catches the 1:34 p.m. westbound bus and arrives at his aunt's apartment just before 2:00 p.m. Together, they catch the northbound 2:12 p.m. bus for a 15-minute ride to the hospital. This bus drops them off right in front of the hospital. The appointment at the hospital is at 2:35 p.m. But today, the city is more crowded than usual because of the Jazz Festival downtown. People are coming to the city from all over the world to attend the festival.

As Jerome arrives at the bus stop on this Thursday, he sees a long line of people waiting to get on. The bus is too full for all the people in line to get on board. The next bus doesn't come until 2:18 p.m. Jerome's aunt needs her routine treatment, and it's difficult to reschedule her appointment. Jerome can't call his aunt because she doesn't have a telephone. He's not sure about what to do next.

Questions

1. What is Jerome's problem?

____

____

____

2. Explain three ways Jerome could do something to solve his problem.

   a. ______________________________

   b. ______________________________

   c. ______________________________

3. Name something Jerome shouldn't do to solve his problem.

   ____

   ____

4. What would you do if you were Jerome? Explain your answer.

   ____

   ____

   ____

   ____

5. Jerome was surprised that he couldn't follow his usual routine to pick up his aunt. What could he have done to avoid this problem?

   ____

   ____

6. What are some good modes of transportation in a big city besides a bus?

   a. ______________________________

   b. ______________________________

   c. ______________________________

   d. ______________________________

General Problem Solving 27

An Award-Winning Hobby

All of her life, Rose has loved to raise things. When she was growing up, she helped raise her younger brother and sister. Then she married and raised four children.

Rose loved flowers and raised them, too. She still does. She didn't have space for a garden so she filled her apartment with pots of flowering plants. Over the years, she discovered she had a knack for raising exotic flowers.

Rose's exotic flowers gained fame in the neighborhood. People stopped to admire the flowers in Rose's windows. If Rose was home, she'd invite them in for a closer look. They'd get a short horticultural lesson and would often take a flower or plant cutting home. Even Rose's children got interested. They'd help Rose care for her flowers and they'd learn a bit of botany along the way.

Rose always wanted a large garden. One day, her children gave her an idea. They suggested she plant flowers around the playground that was in the center of the apartment complex. With their encouragement, permission from the landlord, and help from the neighbors, Rose began planting. Flowers bloomed from early spring to late fall. The playground was filled with fragrance and color and became an important project to everyone in the complex. The landlord started paying Rose for her time and expenses!

The local newspaper interviewed Rose. Pictures of the flower garden were featured on the front page, and in no time, Rose was famous in the city. She was awarded the Mayor's Best Citizen Award for the work she did to beautify the playground. She was invited to speak at town meetings to explain how her hobby grew into an award-winning project.

Rose always told her audiences she never thought her wish for a large garden would happen. She never dreamed she would be recognized for growing flowers in a playground. She reminds her listeners that the best fertilizer for a good idea is neighborly involvement.

Questions

1. What does Rose love to do?
   a. raise kittens
   b. raise the roof
   c. raise flowers

2. How did Rose develop an interest in exotic flowers?

3. Could Rose have planted the playground without the help of her neighbors? Why or why not?

4. Why did the local newspaper find Rose's project interesting?

5. Do you know someone who's turned a project into a business? Tell about it.

General Problem Solving 28

Antique or Everyday?

Antiques are big business today, but some people don't care much about the value of their antiques. They use these old tools every day and can't imagine living without them.

Take Carla Goldberg. She's been offered over $200 for her old rotary lawn mower, but she won't sell it. "I love that old thing," she said. "My yard is small, and I hate the smell of gas-powered mowers, so it's perfect for me. Besides, mowing with it is a good workout."

Ellis Kay loves to make homemade applesauce. "My old apple grinder is over 40 years old," Ellis said. "I've tried to make applesauce with a food processor, but it just doesn't cut the mustard. I don't know if it's worth any money to anyone, but it's certainly priceless to me."

Some antique dealers would probably cringe if they found out how some valuable antiques are being used. The people who own some of these treasures could care less. Cindy Marques keeps a $40,000 Tiffany lamp on an end table in her living room.

"My kids grew up running around that lamp, and I never even knew it was valuable. Once I found out how much it was worth, I couldn't believe it," Ms. Marques said. "But it's a part of our home now. I can't move it or sell it. It's just a lamp to us and always will be."

Questions

1. What item isn't mentioned in this article?
   a. applesauce grinder
   b. Tiffany lamp
   c. Civil War sword
   d. rotary lawn mower

2. Do you think that people should continue using their valuable items? Why or why not?

____

____

3. What are the benefits of using an old-fashioned rotary lawn mower?

____

____

4. Where are three good places (other than an antique store) to find antiques?

   a. ____________

   b. ____________

   c. ____________

5. What are some ways you could find out if an antique was valuable?

____

____

6. Why would an antique dealer be upset if she knew that people were using their antiques every day?

____

____

7. Think of something you use every day that is very old. Why do you continue to use it?

____

____

____

General Problem Solving 29

Step by Step

Last winter was the worst in 35 years in Rock Falls. It was especially bad because of the ice that sealed the city like shrink-wrap. Roads, sidewalks, and peoples' front steps were slick and dangerous for days.

The roads were taken care of by the city. Neighbors banded together and helped to clear the sidewalks, but folks had to clear their front steps themselves. This was particularly difficult for seniors who lived alone.

One morning, Lila Wallace was carefully walking to get her newspaper. The neighbor who usually helps her with these things was caught in snowy traffic and couldn't make it that morning. Lila slipped and broke her left foot. She twisted it so that all the bones in her ankle and foot were fractured.

She's been unable to put weight on it for three months. Now her physician has removed the cast and has put the foot in a soft, walking cast. She's been receiving physical therapy to regain her strength and learn to walk unassisted.

Questions

1. Name two things Lila could have done to get her newspaper without risking slipping on the icy steps.

   a. ______________________________

   b. ______________________________

2. What things will be difficult for Lila to coordinate? Choose all appropriate answers.
   a. which leg to start climbing stairs with
   b. eating steak that hasn't been cut up
   c. which leg to use to hoist herself from a chair
   d. which leg to use to close the front door
   e. brushing her teeth without her electric toothbrush
   f. getting in and out of the bathtub
   g. knitting an afghan for her granddaughter

3. Lila gets discouraged by how slow her recuperation is. Her physical therapist assures her that she is progressing just as the doctor predicted. What do you think the physical therapist would say to Lila to reassure her?
   a. "Don't worry. You can always go back to using a wheelchair."
   b. "You're making steady progress. Remember just last week you couldn't climb stairs."
   c. "Your progress is okay for an elderly person."

4. Lila's goal is to rehabilitate her foot so that she can live independently again at home. The doctor agrees with her goal but is concerned about Lila's safety. Choose all the things below that are safety concerns.
   a. six cracked wooden stairs up to back door
   b. back door hung on two rusty hinges
   c. only one railing on stairs up to front door
   d. large rocking chair
   e. new carpet throughout house
   f. ceramic tile on kitchen wall
   g. laundry facility in basement
   h. all bedrooms on second floor
   i. no affordable snow removal or lawn care services available

5. What would you do if you had an accident and couldn't walk well for three months?

____

____

____

____

General Problem Solving 30

Woodchopping Willie

Willie James has been chopping wood for years. During the Depression, he and his father cut trees together to make a little money to help the family get through the hard times.

If you need a tree cut down, Willie will cut it down by hand even though chainsaws are popular now. He doesn't charge much and all he asks is that in addition to a fee for cutting, he gets to keep your wood. As you can see, he has quite a bit of it. In the autumn, he becomes a very popular fellow. People come from miles around to buy cords of Willie's wood for the winter.

The problem is that Willie can't really compete with local tree-cutting companies who use chainsaws and have many more people to cut trees for them.

The best he can do is to stack his wood in a huge pile by the freeway and hope that people see the pile from the road. If they see Willie and his giant stack of wood, they usually stop. But the local tree-cutting companies want him to stop selling by the side of the road. They say that it's not very good for their businesses. They're lobbying to pass a law which would make it illegal to sell wood by the side of the road.

Questions

1. What is Willie's biggest problem? Explain your answer.

____

____

2. What should Willie do? Choose all of the good solutions.
   a. Calmly negotiate with the big tree-cutting companies.
   b. Refuse to budge from his spot near the freeway.
   c. Steal wood from the large companies.
   d. Get support from local businesses and politicians to fight the proposed law.

3. How can Willie get support to fight the lobbying efforts of the large tree-cutting companies?

____

____

4. What would you propose as a fair solution so that both Willie and the tree-cutting companies can be happy?

____

____

____

____

5. Have you ever been in a situation like Willie's, where a bigger company or group was pressuring you to do something you really didn't want to do? If so, how did it make you feel? What was the solution to the problem? Were all parties satisfied with the result?

____

____

____

____

____

____

____

____

General Problem Solving 31

Philately Nell

Nell's obsession with stamp collecting started with three postage stamps she found in her grandmother's trunk. Nell knew the stamps were old and probably had some value. She had them appraised and discovered they were worth over $1000. She was flabbergasted! She had no idea stamps could be so valuable. That did it—she was hooked on philately.

When Nell was in junior high school, she helped her grandmother steam stamps off of envelopes and catalog them. At that time, she thought stamp collecting was boring. Now she realizes how foolish her thinking was. Nell was eager to find her grandmother's collection. Once found, Nell learned the history of each stamp and eventually started her own business: Philately Nell's Stamp Sensation.

Nell buys, sells, and trades stamps from all over the world. She does research for her customers on stamps they've found or purchased from her. Nell takes her expertise to junior high schools and weaves the history of each stamp into a lively social studies lesson. She wants kids to become excited and avid stamp collectors. She conducts classes after school for kids interested in philately.

Nell knows her grandmother would be surprised and delighted that her hobby caught Nell's attention and became her career.

Questions

1. What do you think *philately* means?

____

____

2. What collections do you have?

3. How did Nell expand her business?

4. What does *flabbergasted* mean?

5. How did Nell's attitude change toward stamp collecting from the time she was a child?

6. Nell is helping young people learn about stamps. Tell about a time when an older person influenced your life. Have you influenced the life of a young person? Explain.

General Problem Solving 32

A Pain in the Back

Getting in shape is a great idea. But for some people, getting in shape means getting hurt. Workout injuries are much more common than they should be, and most of them can be avoided if people follow these few guidelines.

- **See a doctor**. If you haven't exercised for a while, see a doctor before you begin. A doctor might discover a cardiovascular or respiratory problem that you weren't aware of that might place you in danger when you're working out.

- **Know what you're doing**. If you use exercise equipment in a gym, find out how to operate it properly. Motorized treadmills and weight machines can cause serious injuries.

- **Watch the weight**. Weightlifting can cause some very painful injuries. Remember that more repetitions with less weight is better for you and safer than few repetitions with heavy weights. Also, if you have any sort of back problems, stay away from exercises that put stress on your back, like squats.

- **Always work out with a buddy**. This last piece of advice is probably the most important. If you're lifting weights, a partner can give you a hand if you get in trouble. If you're running or riding a bicycle, a buddy can get help if you're injured. Getting in shape should be a fun, rewarding experience. Don't turn it into a potentially dangerous or painful one.

Questions

1. Why do you think so many people decide not to see their doctors before beginning an exercise program?

____

____

2. Which piece of advice was not mentioned in the article?
   a. Work out with a buddy.
   b. See a doctor before beginning an exercise program.
   c. Know how to properly use the equipment.
   d. Warm up thoroughly before you exercise.
   e. Lift light weights for more repetitions.

3. How would cardiovascular or respiratory problems harm you while you're working out?

   ____

   ____

4. What kinds of injuries might motorized treadmills and weight machines cause?

   ______________ ______________

   ______________ ______________

5. What are some ways you could find out how to use the exercise equipment in a gym?

   ____

   ____

6. What painful injuries might heavy weightlifting cause?

   ______________ ______________

   ______________ ______________

7. What are some other advantages you might get from working out with a buddy?

   a. ______________________________

   b. ______________________________

   c. ______________________________

General Problem Solving 33

Betty's Breakdown

Last Sunday, Betty was driving in the far right-hand lane of a five-lane highway outside of Atlanta heading for the suburbs to visit her son. Then her car started giving her trouble.

At first, Betty didn't notice the slight bumpety-bump on the passenger side in front. As she picked up speed, however, the sound and bumping became louder and bumpier. Betty kept driving, though, knowing that she'd see a service station soon. The car started stalling, and Betty pulled over on the shoulder and drove up the shoulder as far as she could.

She was able to pull the car over into the parking lot of a grocery store, but she was still miles from a garage. After she stopped the car, the first thing she did was to get out the cell phone her son bought her and call her road-side service automotive club to get a tow.

Questions

1. Choose all the things that are *positive* about this situation.
   a. The car didn't blow up.
   b. Her two-year-old granddaughter is in the back seat.
   c. Betty has a cell phone to use to call for help.
   d. She's off of the highway and in a commercial parking lot.
   e. Her son lives 20 miles away.
   f. Today is Sunday.
   g. There's no steam coming from the hood.
   h. She is signed up with a road-side service automotive club.

2. Look at the picture. Name all of the emotions that Betty might be experiencing right now.

   a. ______________________________

   b. ______________________________

   c. ______________________________

   d. ______________________________

3. Choose all of the ideas below that might prevent an automobile breakdown or help you if your car breaks down.

   a. If you own a cell phone, always have it in your car.
   b. Join a road-side service motor club.
   c. Make sure you tune the radio to your favorite station.
   d. Have regular maintenance performed on your car according to the manufacturer's recommendations.
   e. Make sure the car is cleaned inside before you take a long trip.
   f. Have your car checked by a reliable mechanic before you drive long distances.
   g. Make sure you wear your seat belt.
   h. Drive the car through a quality car wash regularly.
   i. Buy new tires every 30,000 miles.
   j. Use a top-grade motor oil.
   k. Make sure your spare tire is full of air and ready to use.

4. Have you ever been in an emergency car situation before? Describe the problem and tell about your solution.

   ____

   ____

   ____

   ____

   ____

   ____

General Problem Solving 34

Motorcycle Mania

Mike and his wife, Karen, enjoy riding their motorcycle whenever they can. Whether they ride by themselves or with a group of bikers, they always meet friendly people and have a great time.

Today, they're attending a huge rally at the fairgrounds outside of Detroit. Over 4,000 bikers have come together for the special event. Special parking fields have been set up to handle all the bikes. Inside the fair area, there are bands and food tents set up. Here, a friend is shooting some video of Mike and Karen as they arrive at the rally. After this, everyone went inside and enjoyed a day of music, food, and good times.

When the rally was finished, Mike and Karen came out to the parking lot to get on their motorcycle to make the long ride back home. There was only one problem—they couldn't find their bike. There were so many motorcycles in the parking lot that it took them over an hour to find the right one!

Questions

1. Why would it be hard for Mike and Karen to find their bike?

____

____

2. Based on the story, what do you think a *rally* is?

____

____

3. What suggestions would you give Mike and Karen to help them find their motorcycle the next time.

   a. ______________________________

   b. ______________________________

   c. ______________________________

4. What could Mike and Karen have done to avoid this problem?
   a. parked in an area with a lot of motorcycles
   b. parked in an area with fewer motorcycles
   c. parked in a different rally in a different state

5. Have you ever had trouble finding your car in a parking lot? Explain what happened.

   ____

   ____

6. How do you usually remember where you've parked your car in a crowded lot?

   ____

   ____

7. Remembering where they parked their motorcycle is just one thing Mike and Karen need to think about when they take a ride. What are some other things motorcycle riders need to think about carefully every time they ride?

   a. ______________________________

   b. ______________________________

   c. ______________________________

   d. ______________________________

   e. ______________________________

General Problem Solving 35

An Experiment in Cooperation

Imagine you have a toothache. Wouldn't it be great if someone in your family was a dentist and you could get it taken care of right away? What if you were building a house? It would be great if your dad was an architect and could help you with the plans. Or would it be so great?

"To say Dad and I have had our disagreements would be putting it mildly," Mark Musil says with a grin. "We were at each other's throats for years. He didn't like the decisions I made in high school and he was even more upset with me when I became a journalism major in college. I guess he wanted me to follow in his footsteps and become an architect, too."

Mark's dad, Carl, remembers things about the same way. "He was a wild one in high school," says Carl. "I worried about him all the time, and that worry often became anger. Then in college, he got this journalism idea in his head. I wanted him to try for something more practical, but I guess it's all worked out."

Mark just published his third book, is a syndicated newspaper columnist, and he and his wife Linda just welcomed their third child into the family. They decided the time had come to build their dream house. "Linda thought we should ask Dad to help right away," Mark says. "I wasn't so sure. Our history of cooperation hasn't been so great. But Dad's extremely talented, and the more I thought about having him design our house, the more excited I got."

"I guess we've both grown up over the past few years," Carl says. "There were some uncomfortable moments when we first started talking about the design, but I think we both started to see what a unique opportunity we had in front of us." The design is almost complete, and they expect to break ground next spring. It seems this house has become a dream come true for the entire Musil family.

Questions

1. There are several people mentioned in this story. Which person is not mentioned?
   a. Mark Musil
   b. Linda Musil
   c. the Musil children
   d. Mark's dad, Carl
   e. Mark's mother, Maureen

2. What would be some downsides to having a dentist in your family?

   ____

   ____

3. What does it mean to *follow in someone's footsteps*?

   ____

   ____

4. How can you cooperate with someone that you don't get along with very well?

   ____

   ____

   ____

   ____

5. What are some strategies Mark and his dad might use to avoid disagreements while they are working on the house?

   a. ____

   b. ____

   c. ____

General Problem Solving 36

Enzo's Big Party

Tina's father's 75th birthday was two months away, and she wanted to have a special party to celebrate the occasion. So she called her family and together they planned a party their dad would not forget—they would reenact a Bocce tournament.

Tina's dad, Enzo, was the 1943 Bocce ball champion in Italy. To reenact the event, the family located as many of the former Italian teammates as they could find. They built Bocce courts and purchased regulation Bocce balls. They collected their dad's tournament memorabilia and displayed it. They invited neighbors and close friends. They made Enzo's favorite Italian foods.

All but two members of the Italian Bocce team came. Most of their friends and neighbors came, too. Enzo was amazed. The teammates reminisced, swapped war stories, told Bocce tales, and played Bocce all night. Enzo had the time of his life. He told his family he felt 20 years younger.

Questions

1. What preparations were made for Enzo's party?

   a. ______________________________

   b. ______________________________

   c. ______________________________

   d. ______________________________

   e. ______________________________

2. Why was this birthday special for Enzo?

____

____

3. By looking at the picture, can you explain how the game of Bocce might be played?

____

____

4. What does *reminisce* mean?

____

____

5. If your friends or family threw you a special birthday party, what are some things you'd like to have happen?

location: ____

____

favorite foods: ____

____

music: ____

____

special people you would want at your party: ____

____

activities you would enjoy: ____

____

General Problem Solving 37

Heading Back to School

Some people would call 38-year-old Robert Blum crazy. Last fall he gave up his $120,000 a year salary as a stockbroker to become a high school civics teacher who barely makes $30,000. Robert laughs as he thinks about the night he told his mother. "She just kept shaking her head," he said. "Her tongue was completely tied. She didn't know what to say."

So why did he make such a dramatic change? "Basically, money is boring," Robert says. "It doesn't disobey you, it doesn't talk back, and it doesn't learn anything. My entire day was spent trying to make more of this boring stuff for my clients and myself. I needed a change, and becoming a teacher was about the biggest one I could think of."

"When I went to work as a stockbroker, the first thing I'd do in the morning was flip on my computers and hit the phones," Robert says. "Now I get to work and interact with people I really like and respect. And teaching civics to high school kids is an even bigger challenge than cold-calling clients and trying to get them to invest with me. The rewards of teaching are a hundred times better than the return on any money investment."

Actually, the decision to change careers wasn't that hard for Robert to make. He had been trained as a teacher in college and held a valid teaching certificate. Teaching was what he really wanted to do when he graduated, but money became very important to him at that time. "When I got out of school, I looked at the student loan debts I had and realized it would be tough to pay them back on a teacher's salary," Robert says. "So I looked into becoming a stockbroker and I became certified."

Everyone asks Robert the same question these days—are you happy you made the change? "Absolutely," he answers, "but don't misunderstand me here; I'm no idealist. I made a lot of money over the last 15 years, and I invested it well. Now I have the freedom to take a job I love, even if it doesn't pay much."

Questions

1. What professions are mentioned in this passage?
    a. school principal
    b. teacher
    c. stockbroker

2. When Robert told his mother he was quitting his stockbroker job, he said her "tongue was completely tied." What did Robert mean by that?

3. Would you agree that "money is boring"? Why or why not?

4. Robert didn't go into teaching after college because he had debts to pay off. How could he have taken a teaching job and still have had money to pay off his debts?

5. What problems might Robert face in his new career? Do you think he'll stick with it or go back to being a stockbroker? Why?

General Problem Solving 38

Staying in Touch

Frank Stanton is a retired librarian. He lives in Pennsylvania by himself. His wife died two years ago and his children and grandchildren live in Texas and Montana. He doesn't see them very often, but he likes to stay in touch with them by telephone.

His kids have tried to persuade their dad to get a computer so he can E-mail them. Frank's hearing is poor, and it's getting harder and harder for him to hear people over the telephone. He can't understand what his grandchildren say at all, and he can barely hear his daughter's voice. He hears his son and his son-in-law more clearly.

His children think he's being stubborn. They have offered to pitch in and buy him a computer so he can use E-mail, but Frank insists that he can still hear just fine. He says the telephone is good enough for him—he doesn't need a computer just so he can stay in touch.

Questions

1. Why doesn't Frank see his children or grandchildren very often?

____

____

2. What is E-mail?

____

____

3. Do you stay in touch with the people who are important to you? If not, why aren't you in touch with them as much as you'd like?

____

____

____

____

4. Do you think Frank is being stubborn about his refusal to use a computer to communicate? Why or why not?

____

____

____

5. Why is it harder for Frank to hear his grandchildren than it is to hear his son and son-in-law?

____

____

6. What are some other ways Frank and his children could stay in contact without using a telephone?

   a. ____________________

   b. ____________________

   c. ____________________

   d. ____________________

   e. ____________________

General Problem Solving 39

Moving Day

Sarah has lived in her house for 35 years. Now it's time to move to a smaller apartment. To get ready for the move, she's going from room to room to decide what to do with all of her things. Today, she's tackling the closet in her guest room.

Most of the clothes in this closet have hung here undisturbed for several years. In fact, the only thing she still uses from this closet are the rolls of wrapping paper.

Sarah doesn't like things to go to waste, so she's thinking of ways to get the clothes, blankets, and everything else to people who might use them. Everyone seems to have an opinion about what she should do with all of the stuff in her closet.

Here are some of the options she's considering:

- Ask the local amateur theater group if they'd like any of the things for costumes or props.
- Give the blankets to the Red Cross.
- Call the Salvation Army and ask them to pick everything up.
- Ask her church to store the things until they have their next clothing drive.

Questions

1. Why doesn't Sarah put her things in boxes and take them with her when she moves?

____

____

____

2. Why do you think many of the clothes in the picture are in clear plastic bags? Choose all appropriate answers.
   a. The clothes don't fit anymore.
   b. She hasn't worn the clothes in years.
   c. She doesn't like the clothes anymore.

3. What does the expression *go to waste* mean?

   ____

   ____

4. Which of Sarah's ideas do you think are good ones? List them below.
   a. ______________________________
   b. ______________________________
   c. ______________________________
   d. ______________________________

5. Give Sarah some other suggestions on how to get rid of her old clothes.
   a. ______________________________
   b. ______________________________
   c. ______________________________
   d. ______________________________

6. Would it be easy or difficult for you to sort through the things you don't use anymore? Why or why not?

   ____

   ____

   ____

General Problem Solving 40

Dad for a Day

David leads a pretty quiet life. He's a 28-year-old bachelor who is the co-owner of a small restaurant. His serene little life got a little more interesting Saturday afternoon.

"My sister needed to go to an emergency meeting at work, and her husband was out of town for the weekend," David said. "She called me and asked if I would be able to watch her son, Danny, for a few hours."

He says, "I wasn't so sure at first. I'd never been alone with a two-year-old, but the panic in her voice convinced me that this was something I needed to do for my sister." David's sister threw open his front door 15 minutes after the phone call, plopped Danny down on David's new white couch, and dropped what seemed like ten bags of baby supplies in the middle of the floor. She gave David and Danny each a quick kiss, then let go with a stream of words so quick David only caught a few of them. He thought he heard "life saver, appreciate, already ate," and the dreaded "needs to be changed." The door then slammed and she was gone.

"I just kind of sat there looking at Danny climb around on the couch for a minute," David said. "Then I caught my breath and realized if I was going to do this, I'd better dive right in." David got his nephew changed, then pulled out some of Danny's toys, and they played together on the floor for a while.

"After you get down on the floor with a toddler, you get in the swing of things fast," David laughed. "I had a couple of awkward moments there, but after that, it was a lot of fun. We played, we had a snack, we ran around outside, and then we watched TV for a few minutes until he fell asleep. Not long after, my sister came through the front door again. She was much calmer this time as she gathered up Danny and his things. I'm already looking forward to the next time he can come over and play."

Questions

1. What things at the beginning of this story tell you that David might not enjoy having a two-year-old around?

   a. ______________________________

   b. ______________________________

2. Why might David's sister have been so panicked and rushed when she came into his house?

   ____

   ____

3. Read the last part of the third paragraph again. David mentions that he only heard a few words his sister said as she hurried out the door. Use these words to recreate exactly what his sister might have said.

   ____

   ____

   ____

   ____

   ____

   ____

4. Why did getting down on the floor with the toddler loosen David up?

   ____

   ____

   ____

   ____

Answer Key

Problem Solving

pp. 6-7

1. c, c
2. b, a
3. b, c
4. **Problem:** Family members are asking for loans.
   Solution: Explain why you can't loan money.
5. **Problem:** Your daughter can't make the down payment on a house.
   Solution: Loan her the money for the down payment; help her make a plan to save the money.
6. **Problem:** The IRS is auditing you and you've never gone through an audit.
   Solution: Find out what information you will need for the IRS; contact an accountant.
7. **Problem:** Your doctor is no longer affiliated with your insurance plan.
   Solution: Change doctors; keep the same doctor and save money elsewhere.

pp. 8-9

1. a, c
2. c, b
3. c, a
4. **Problem:** You're not supposed to go to work on icy days.
   Solution: Have someone pick you up at your door and drop you off at the door at work.
5. **Problem:** Your daughter is using the company's toll-free number.
   Solution: Have her call on a local line.
6. **Problem:** Having customers in your home bothers your daughter.
   Solution: Set a certain time for clients to pick up their work.
7. **Problem:** You already have plans the day your boss asks you to play golf.
   Solution: Tell your boss you already have plans but would like to play golf some other day.

pp. 10-11

1. c, a
2. b, a
3. c, b
4. **Problem:** Two friends you want to invite over don't like one another.
   Solution: Invite them both but let each know the other has been invited.
5. **Problem:** Your grandchildren bring friends to your house who are are noisy.
   Solution: Ask them not to bring friends when they come over for video night.
6. **Problem:** You are embarrassed to have a rusty car parked in front of your house.
   Solution: Help your neighbor find a different place to park his car.
7. **Problem:** You think your neighbor's dog wrecked your new plants.
   Solution: Ask your neighbors to keep their dog out of your yard.

pp. 12-13

1. b, a
2. b, c
3. b, c
4. **Problem:** You have two appointments at the same time.
   Solution: Go to one and reschedule the other.
5. **Problem:** A young child is walking down the street alone.
   Solution: Bring the child into your home and locate her parents.
6. **Problem:** A friend wants to start a workout program without seeing his doctor first.
   Solution: Suggest that your friend start slow and work his way up to a rigorous level.
7. **Problem:** Your friend is choking.
   Solution: Perform the Heimlich maneuver on him or call for help.

pp. 14-16

1. c, b
2. b, a
3. c, b
4. **Problem:** You have ruined one of your neighbor's prize orchids.
   Solution: Apologize to your neighbor and offer to replace it.
5. **Problem:** The people in front of you at a sporting event are annoying.
   Solution: Move to an empty seat elsewhere.
6. **Problem:** You find the language offensive in a movie you are watching.
   Solution: Leave the theater and wait for your friend outside.
7. **Problem:** You have two invitations for dinner on the same night.
   Solution: Suggest you all have dinner together.
8. **Problem:** You can't remember where to meet your friend at the mall.
   Solution: Go to the doors leading to the parking lot and wait there for your friend.

Note: Your clients' answers will vary on many of these tasks. Sample answers have been provided to assist you in cueing and modeling.

Answer Key

9. **Problem:** You have a flat tire and can't find the jack to fix it.
   Solution: Check the user's manual to see where the jack is located.
10. **Problem:** You and your spouse want to do different things on your vacation.
    Solution: Take turns doing what each likes on different days.
11. **Problem:** Neighborhood boys make too much noise outside your window.
    Solution: Ask them to play elsewhere or close your windows.

Analyzing Problems

p. 18
1. c
2. no
3. The current balance is all that is due.

p. 19
1. b
2. It is a fee for using an ATM in another city.
3. b

p. 20
1. c
2. b
3. Budget your money better so you have enough to pay the bill.

1. You would have room for your family members to stay when they visit.
2. Ask them to bring sleeping bags so they can sleep on the floor or have them stay in a motel.

p. 21
1. Frank's Records
2. a
3. b

p. 22
1. $495
2. 3
3. Oct. 22
4. 6
5. Mink Community College
6. no
7. 15 or less

p. 23
1. $200,000
2. $14,000 ($200,000 x .07)
3. $186,000 ($200,000 – $14,000)
4. $202,500 ($200,000 + $2,500)

1. half a day
2. noon on Wednesday
3. at home, the library, a friend's house

p. 24
1. products in the mortgage and financial industry
2. call 1-800-322-3562
3. $1400-$1800
4. excellent benefits
5. $280

p. 25
1. 125
2. $375
3. $6,500
4. $150
5. $375
6. 2
7. in the apartment complex
8. $500
9. no
10. 50
11. She needs $1,000 and you need to check references.

p. 26
1. a
2. a
3. a

p. 27
1. 4
2. 1-800-555-2222
3. 2
4. $30
5. no
6. no

p. 28
1. b
2. $139.95
3. 50
4. none
5. $45 (free if you purchase portraits)
6. call for appointment

p. 29
1. c
2. $.87
3. chicken salad sandwich
4. $2.56

pp. 30-31
1. b
2. c
3. b
4. c
5. yes, 3
6. prescription number
7. 30 minutes before the first food, beverage, or medication of the day
8. No; you need to take it with water.
9. You should not lie down for 30 minutes after taking it.

p. 32
1. b
2. a
3. Dr. Stephen Johnson
4. yes

Note: Your clients' answers will vary on many of these tasks. Sample answers have been provided to assist you in cueing and modeling.

Answer Key

p. 33

1. b
2. page the doctor
3. morning

pp. 34-35

1. a
2. a
3. a
4. b
5. d
6. Big Town
7. October 5
8. c
9. Ontario, Sept. 14

p. 37

1. b
2. a
3. c
4. Excellent; it was named "Best Decor" by *Inside Resort* magazine.
5. call or fax
6. $290 per person
7. Two people must be in a room.

p. 38

1. b
2. b
3. a
4. a
5. 2:00 pm
6. no
7. closer
8. no
9. coat, jacket, or sweatshirt

Understanding & Applying Information

pp. 40-41

1. • one that changes
   • one that stays the same
   • you won't make as much money
2. The extra charge is a handling or convenience fee.
3. games, books, toys, sporting goods, etc.
4. The phone company might take those charges off your bill.
5. b
6. b
   A grace period is a period of time to pay your balance when you won't be charged a finance fee.
7. Call information or your credit card company and get the current number for the catalog company and call them.
8. They are the same value.
9. the 10-minute card
10. c

pp. 42-43

1. a, c
   a, b
2. b, c
   a, b
3. a, c
   It won't get done right or in a timely manner.
4. dish soap, window cleaner, diluted ammonia or bleach
5. • The co-worker might tell others about this information.
   • Your co-worker might get in serious trouble or get fired.
6. • Look carefully for everything that is missing and have someone help you look.
   • Ask him if anyone else was in the house with him while he cleaned; ask him if he moved any of the items when he was cleaning.

pp. 44-45

1. b, d, e, f
2. a, c, d, e
3. They are divorced or separated.
4. Sell the furniture, put it in storage, or give it away.
5. • You need to know what sizes she wears now.
   • She could return them for the right size.
   • Buy her a gift certificate.
6. • You could go to one house or the other or you could stay home.
   • You could find out who the other guests at the homes will be to see who you want to spend time with.
7. Look in the newspaper or on the Internet.
8. You could put up a fence.

pp. 46-47

1. a, b, d, e, f
2. a, c, d, f, g
3. • You may have pulled a muscle, pinched a nerve, or strained your back.
   • You could go to the doctor or apply heat or ice.
   • Bend your knees and lift straight up using your legs instead of your back.
4. • Lock all doors and windows, cover windows with plywood, and be ready to go to a safe location.
   • You need to know when the storm is expected to hit and its severity.
   • You can stay home or go to a safer location.

Note: Your clients' answers will vary on many of these tasks. Sample answers have been provided to assist you in cueing and modeling.

Answer Key

5. • Talk to your neighbors about your idea.
   • Have them be on their porches to monitor activities and keep all their lights on.
   • Organize a Halloween party in a central location.
6. • Start an exercise program
   • hiking/biking trails, fitness center, YMCA
   • You need to know how far you will be walking or hiking each day.
7. • Make a chart and check them off when they've been taken or carry a compartmentalized pill organizer.
   • Your family, friends, or a nurse could help you.

pp. 48-50

1. a, b
   a
2. b
   a
3. a, c
   a
4. b, c
   a, b
5. c
   a
   bathing suit, toiletries, casual clothes, formal clothes, money, medication, etc.
6. c; b
   a, c
7. b; b
   tire inflation, effectiveness of brakes, proper lubrication of all parts, safety equipment

Paraphrasing & Summarizing

pp. 52-53

1. b; c
2. c; a
3. c
4. • Your phone will be turned off by May 13 if we don't receive payment.
   • You might have to pay a fee to get your phone service turned back on.
5. You need to pay the bill by the 21st of next month.
6. Answers will vary.
7. Answers will vary.

pp. 54-55

1. c
2. b
3. a
4. • Your friend thinks you spend your money foolishly.
   • Do you really think that is a good way to spend your money?
5. Answers will vary.
6. Answers will vary.
7. software engineer, journalist, technical writer, editor, network specialist, tour guide, etc.

pp. 56-57

1. c
2. d
3. • You're blocking his view.
   • He could politely ask you to sit down because he can't see.
4. Your looks haven't changed.
5. very dressy, formal attire required
6. Cook something to bring instead; remind them of your preference.
7. Your teacher likes the good questions you ask in class and enjoys your participation in discussion.
8. He wants your mom to stay at home more often.
9. Tell her that you enjoy being alone and aren't ready to date at this time.
10. Some of your family members object to your brother's new wife and aren't afraid to express their opinions.

pp. 58-59

1. c
2. a
3. c
4. b; b
5. c; b
6. a; c
7. b; a

pp. 60-62

1. • It's a small group of items that were made at the same time.
   • a person who buys and sells antiques
   • Your porcelain figurine collection does not include a limited edition choir boy.
2. • a student with a learning disability, a student who does not learn new things easily
   • He does not want you to talk about individual students' learning problems outside the school.
3. • You have to pay for them yourself and are not included in the package price.
   • Would you like to go on a mystery bus trip with me? It costs $25, and you need to

Note: Your clients' answers will vary on many of these tasks. Sample answers have been provided to assist you in cueing and modeling.

Answer Key

dress warmly and wear comfortable shoes. Lunch and snacks aren't included in the package price.

4. You are in good shape.
5. a, b, c
6. c
7. • both ways
   • two people to a room
   • a
8. • There are players on first, second, and third base.
   • It's a home run when the bases are loaded.
   • changed pitchers
   • home run
9. • The kids will not only learn how to do something, they will actually do it.
   • Answers will vary.

Making Inferences

pp. 64-65

1. c
2. b, c
3. c
4. No; you must be a qualified buyer.
5. Since it was an old catalog, the sweater might be on sale, discounted, or on clearance since it is no longer a new item.
6. • No; the sign says "Free Estimates."
   • They need to make sure that you are seriously interested since they will have a difficult time selling the frame to someone else if you back out of the sale.
   • No; they will customize any size frame to fit your needs.
7. • She forgot to enter the deposits because she was ill.
   • Talk to the bank and tell them the situation; put more money in her account and have her pay you back later.

pp. 66-67

1. a, b
2. a
3. You should help your own neighborhood before you go help another neighborhood.
4. • He does not trust the new assistant with confidential information, such as salary information.
   • He does not seem happy about it.
5. You should expect a pay increase.
6. She feels uncomfortable about working on a project outside of her regular job responsibilities.
7. The company is not afraid of using new ideas or setting guidelines that differ from conservative ways.
8. You spend more time paying attention to your job than to your spouse.
9. You were given the promotion due to luck, not based on your ability or performance.
10. No

pp. 68-69

1. a, b
2. c, b
3. b, a
4. c, a
5. b, a
6. a, c

pp. 70-71

1. Two hearing aids are best, but if you can only afford one, it would still help quite a bit.
2. You'll lose weight.
3. water aerobics
4. c
5. • No
   • Yes; daily assistance is provided.
   • Yes; meal preparation is provided.
   • Use the 24-hour emergency nursing response service.
6. You will recover very quickly.
7. The snow is coming down so hard that you can't see clearly even a few feet in front of you.

pp. 72-74

1. b
2. c, a
3. b, c
4. Be courteous to the next person who will rent the video by rewinding the tape to the beginning; you would expect your tape to be at the beginning when you rent it, so you should do it for the next person.
5. He was dealt a good set of cards.
6. These cards would be a great Christmas gift idea for her.
7. • You need to continue to practice the lesson because there are still a few places in the song that could use a bit more practicing.
   • Answers will vary.
8. There are runners in scoring position.
9. Your friend did not enjoy the show and regrets going to it.
10. • The ballpark does not assume liability if anyone is injured by a baseball or baseball bat.
    • You could be struck with a baseball or baseball bat if you are not paying attention or watching carefully.

Note: Your clients' answers will vary on many of these tasks. Sample answers have been provided to assist you in cueing and modeling.

Answer Key

Empathizing

pp. 76-77

1. • a
   • nervous, pressured, anxious, excited
2. • b
   • feelings hurt, disappointed
3. • upset, irresponsible, nervous
   • You left it at the video store.
4. You might feel obligated to help her financially.
5. pressured, uncomfortable
6. Frustrated, annoyed, aggravated, confused; the checking account that was opened was not the one you wanted.
7. You might feel taken advantage of.
8. embarrassed, angry

pp. 78-79

1. a, b
2. • c
   • Explain to him what you do when you have some down time to keep busy.
3. b, c
4. • b
   • It is only fair that you assume some of the burden that she has been handling for many years.
5. c, b, c

pp. 80-81

1. • Explain honestly why you want him to leave the dog at home.
   • He will probably be sad but understanding.
2. • embarrassed, unappreciated
   • That was very inconsiderate of me. Sometimes I talk before I think. I'm sorry.
3. • She might be hurt and embarrassed, or she might feel angry that you are trying to make someone feel guilty.
   • Young people sometimes do not consider the feelings of others and you shouldn't take it personally.
4. • She is scared and doesn't want to leave her home and move into a nursing home.
   • The doctor is frustrated that your neighbor doesn't watch her diet or take care of herself properly.
   • Answers will vary.
5. • You might be insulted that she considers your possessions "old stuff."
   • Thanks so much for the offer, but I don't really have a place to keep such things.
   • Answers will vary.

pp. 82-83

1. c
2. b, c
3. b, c; a
4. Slow down and consider giving up the things that you really don't want to do and don't have time for, and reprioritize your life so you have time to do some things that you enjoy.
5. Say something general about all babies, like "babies are so darling."
6. I'm sorry for being so inconsiderate. Would you like a few more minutes before you see me?
7. You could have walked over, steadied the ladder, and urged him to be careful up there.

pp. 84-86

1. c, a
2. • You are unhappy that your team is about to lose.
   • You are excited that your team won.
3. • He is sorry that one of the guests is unhappy with the type of music that he brought.
   • Do you have any other CDs we could play to mix up the music?
4. • He is appreciative of what he learned from his coach, excited about his award, and thrilled to share the excitement with his coach.
   • thrilled, excited, shocked
5. He is proud that he received a silver medal, but sad that he did not win the gold medal.
6. • She doesn't like them and feels unappreciated by them.
   • She could have her husband encourage her in-laws to be more understanding of her feelings.
7. • aggravated, irritated, appalled that he is not moving
   • inconvenienced, obstinate, stubborn
   • You could offer to sit in another seat if one is available.
8. • sorry, irresponsible, embarrassed
   • She is regretful that she let you borrow the basketball.
   • Buy her a new ball; give her money to buy a new ball.
   • relieved, satisfied

Note: Your clients' answers will vary on many of these tasks. Sample answers have been provided to assist you in cueing and modeling.

Evaluating

pp. 88-89

1. c, a
2. a, a and b
3. c, a
4. a, c
5. c, a

pp. 90-91

1. personal abilities and skills, finances, availability of jobs
2. Consider how well she takes care of your daughter and compare costs against other providers.
3. cost of living of place you are moving to, new responsibilities of a new job, feelings of your spouse and children, hassle of moving
4. **Pros**
   - company will be able to handle more calls
   - system will save money

   Cons
   - costs $75,000
   - not personal
5. sugar free or low-fat treats that still taste good
6. customer feedback, delivery time, reliability
7. family considerations, social life considerations, if the extra money meets needs better no matter what time shift he works
8. personal finances, needs of your child
9. personal finances, career change
10. children's caregiver, emotional or physical needs of the children

pp. 92-93

1. b, a
2. b
3. c, b
4. a
5. Consult your friends before you leave to see where they'd like to go.
6. You could have been more explicit, told your spouse exactly what to get, or bought them yourself.
7. Choose a variety of music appropriate for each age group.

pp. 94-95

1. doctor visits, good diet, exercise
2. Research different diets and weight loss methods.
3. Pretend you are the height of the toddler, walk around your home, and remove items that are unsafe for a baby; ask a parent of a young child for advice.
4. If the exercises help you feel better and you feel motivated to go to the class, the instructor is probably doing a good job.
5. Ask the people you are staying with or consult with the concierge or desk clerk at the hotel.
6. Ask the salesperson at the furniture store or read the manufacturer's information on the tag of the furniture.
7. If, at the end of the three months you have lost some weight or feel better, the diet is probably working.
8. Choose the store with the better produce section.
9. years in business, stock price, financial soundness of company, growth potential
10. taste and presentation
11. Pick a resort that has a mixture of outdoor and indoor activities, including an indoor swimming pool.
12. Research information regarding the preventative measures a person living in an earthquake zone should take; have your home inspected by a professional.
13. Ask your doctor; hire a personal trainer for assistance.

pp. 96-98

1. Determine what specific things you are looking for in a sports team and then spend time watching or talking with team members.
2. affordability, quality, warranty information
3. Join a singles group.
4. Contact the police.
5. She may think you are depressed or simply don't know how to have a social life on your own.
6. - She thinks you are aggressive, insensitive, and overly ambitious.
   - She is unsure that she is ready to retire.
7. - Monitor or limit his use of the Internet.
   - You might feel that he is depressed or that something is wrong.
8. - embarrassed, ashamed, frustrated
   - He wants her to do better and if he yells at her, maybe she will improve or he doesn't think she was trying her best.
   - Answers will vary.
9. - She thinks Gabby exercises too much and that she was bound to get hurt.
   - She could have said she was worried for her and she is sorry that she had been hurt.

Note: Your clients' answers will vary on many of these tasks. Sample answers have been provided to assist you in cueing and modeling.

General Problem Solving

pp. 100-101

1. • generous
   She helps others financially and is a life-long community volunteer of her time.
   • lucky
   She has has won a digital camera and $500,000 in prizes over the last year.
   • caring
   She constantly helps others.
2. It's faster and more convenient.
3. She could have gotten their phone number and called them back to make sure they were legitimate.
4. No; it is a common reaction when you are shocked.
5. income taxes, how she will spend the money, what others will think, how it will change her life.
6. Answers will vary.
7. a call that is a practical joke

pp. 102-103

1. Have the relatives RSVP to ensure they received the invitations.
2. The following items should be checked: call guests, arrange for entertainment, design invitations, prepare/cook food, make hotel plans for guests, include directions, plan a menu
3. They could provide a large selection of common foods; have each family bring a dish to share.
4. She is willing to do the work, but feels that it should be shared between the other family members.
5. Answers will vary.

pp. 104-105

1. c
2. They boxed up 3 of their 4 TVs and stuck them in a closet; they decided to only turn the TV on if something was on that they really wanted to see.
3. The TV monopolized time in her schedule that could have been spent doing something productive.
4. It provides background noise and gives people the sense that they are not alone.
5. Answers will vary.
6. Talk more; listen to music; take up a new hobby.
7. Answers will vary.

pp. 106-107

1. b
2. She could try to convince the other writers that proofreading hard copy is the best way for her to proofread their work.
3. You can explain to me why you think it is better for me to proofread online, but I still won't believe that it is better than proofing via hard copy.
4. She may be fired if she doesn't comply with the company's views.
5. c
6. The following items should be checked "yes": Job counseling, Adjusting to change, and Technology for Today. How to invest your 401(k) funds should be checked "no."
7. Answers will vary.

pp. 108-109

1. Answers will vary.
2. She doesn't mind being one of the first patients to undergo the procedure.
3. 4, 1, 3, 2, 5
4. Answers will vary.
5. nervous, anxious
6. Answers will vary.
7. She will be no worse off if the new procedure fails because she hasn't responded to traditional procedures and medicines.

pp. 110-111

1. c
2. She could have one of the store employees page him or start walking around the store looking for him.
3. She might apologize for not considering his feelings.
4. His feet hurt, his head aches, his back aches, he wants to sit for awhile, and he doesn't know where his wife is.
5. He is tired and achy and would like to go home.
6. c
7. Answers will vary.

pp. 112-113

1. a notebook you write in
2. They were not aware all the while Harvey knew them he was writing stories about them.
3. They might complain to Harvey or ask him to change the manuscript in order to make them happy.
4. honored, excited, embarrassed, angered, proud
5. It brought back many memories of their own; it reminds them of their youth and their accomplishments over their lifetime.
6. Answers will vary.

Note: Your clients' answers will vary on many of these tasks. Sample answers have been provided to assist you in cueing and modeling.

Answer Key

pp. 114-115
1. c
2. b, c
3. Traveling means many hours away from home and away from her family.
4. working from her home, traveling less hours, working part-time, find another job
5. telephone, e-mail, FAX, post-cards
6. You don't need to think about it.

pp. 116-117
1. Expanding a business means taking on more responsibilities and risk, as well as investing more money.
2. someone who does not have use of the lower half of her body due to paralysis
3. b, c, d, e
4. financial investments, risk, employee concerns, personal preference, increased responsibility
5. a, b, d
6. Answers will vary.

pp. 118-119
1. The purpose is to build one-on-one friendships and companionship between mature adults and children who need more adult influence in their lives.
2. It gives them a sense of security.
3. b
4. library, sporting events, fishing, bicycling, movies, concerts, etc.
5. Answers will vary.
6. Marcus may lose his ambition to read or stop exploring opportunities that Jared has introduced to him.

pp. 120-121
1. Are you well enough to continue or should we return home?
2. a, c, e, f
3. She might have been regretful that she had tried to do too much by herself.
4. You are brave to try to take on such a responsibility by herself.
5. no running, what to do in case someone is lost, what to do in case someone feels ill
6. Answers will vary.

p. 123
1. e
2. competitions, exercise programs, counseling, group activities
3. Answers will vary.
4. Answers will vary.

p. 125
1. b, c
2. Older adults have more years of memories and history than teenagers.
3. experience with scrap booking, an ability to get people thinking about important events in their lives
4. Answers will vary.
5. Answers will vary.

pp. 126-127
1. to combine the two companies into one larger company
2. Some employees could lose their jobs due to an overlap in job responsibilities.
3. a, b, c, d
4. a, b, c, d, e
5. a, c, d, e, g

p. 129
1. b, c, d
2. Visual aids such as slides and computer images were not easily accessible early in Sarah's teaching career.
3. They could publicize the urgent need for teachers and create incentives for new teachers.
4. She was in control of her classroom and expected students to follow her rules.
5. Answers will vary.

pp. 130-131
1. clothing, specialty gifts, holiday decorations, jewelry, toys
2. They understand that part of the holiday is fighting the crowds and that it is courteous to help others.
3. a. You will be on your feet a long time.
   b. You will probably be shopping for hours so wear something you won't want to change.
   c. There will be long lines and losing your temper won't make them go any faster.
   d. You may not have time to stop for lunch because of the time it will take to do your shopping.
   e. You will be in line for more time than usual, so be prepared and bring a book or something to do.
   f. Shopping is sometimes hard work and you wouldn't want to get dehydrated.

p. 133
1. outgoing, hard-working, ambitious, all lost strength and vitality after their health declined

Note: Your clients' answers will vary on many of these tasks. Sample answers have been provided to assist you in cueing and modeling.

Answer Key

2. They all lost their strength and vitality.
3. She understood all the accomplishments that Helen, Eugene and Sybil had made in their lives and they needed a way to regain the use of those talents.
4. **Helen**
   before: outgoing, life of the party
   after: organizer, scheduled exercise room space
   Eugene
   before: farmed, grain research, refurbished parks
   after: brought plants into exercise area
   Sybil
   before: hairdresser, choir director, guitar teacher, chef
   after: played guitar for sing-alongs

p. 135
1. a
2. loss of a job, death of a pet, divorce, catastrophic injury
3. No; only 78% of his clients have reported success.
4. Kara's sister invited her to lunch, but instead she took her to see a counselor who specialized in grief recovery; answers will vary.
5. to make a big change or change something dramatically

p. 137
1. Their business became more efficient and allowed the family to take vacations once the crops were planted.
2. No; he agreed with his philosophy about never taking a vacation.
3. He never took a vacation.
4. They both believed that they needed to be running the farm every day and that there was no time for vacations.
5. Answers will vary.

p. 139
1. a, b, d, f
2. diabetic restrictions, food allergies, nutritional concerns, preparation limitations, cost of ingredients
3. They can learn a lot from one another and understand one another better if they spend time together.
4. **Students:** gain skills, take on responsibility, feel good about helping others
   Seniors: enjoy seeing the kids and interacting with them, get to eat good food

pp. 140-141
1. The camera that they purchased especially for their trip is not working properly.
2. Ask someone else who is attending the reunion to take pictures and send them copies; buy an inexpensive camera to use while their camera is being fixed; buy a disposable camera.
3. They want to take pictures of the specific sites they see in Napa and include pictures of their relatives in them.
4. Contact the manufacturer or the store where they bought it.
5. Save your receipt and save your product and warranty information.
6. c
7. True

p. 143
1. Many of her friends were reluctant to take advantage of offshore fishing because of their physical limitations.
2. She worked with several professionals in the area to lease and equip a boat especially for seniors.
3. Avoid rough waters, make sure the boat is equipped with emergency equipment, have plenty of help on hand, and make sure there is clear communication to shore.
4. Her market is designed for senior citizens.
5. Answers will vary.

pp. 144-145
1. a
2. to prevent your hair from getting messed up, equipment is uncomfortable, takes too long to put all the equipment on
3. a. It protects your head from injury in case of a fall.
   b. It helps you be more aerodynamic.
4. The helmet could cut into your head if it is too small or it could fall off or out of place if it is too large.
5. hockey, football, skateboarding, baseball
6. a hero or a savior; no
7. Answers will vary.

pp. 146-147
1. 15 years
2. c
3. a
4. Yes; she would have enjoyed a different career; she may be more self-confident now.
5. a. Set goals and strive to achieve them.

Note: Your clients' answers will vary on many of these tasks. Sample answers have been provided to assist you in cueing and modeling.

Answer Key

b. Don't wait until it's too late to follow your dreams.
c. Don't let health problems get in the way of your dreams.
d. Even though there may be a few bumps along the way, nothing is impossible
e. Don't settle for less than what you want.

6. When talking to high school students, she might be more focused on the future; for senior citizens, she would be focused on the present.

pp. 148-149

1. Both the music and the people might be considered "golden" (valuable, classic) and "oldies" (because of their ages and the age of the music).
2. a, d
3. They are all retired music teachers, and it is a way for them to get together and continue doing what they love to do.
4. Add dance steps to the songs they sing.
5. Answers will vary.
6. b
7. Answers will vary.

pp. 150-151

1. If he doesn't get on the bus, his aunt may miss her doctor appointment.
2. a. Explain his situation and get in front of the line.
   b. Check the subway or train schedule.
   c. Call his aunt's apartment manager and see if he/she could take her.
3. Simply wait in line or lose his temper and start yelling.
4. Answers will vary.
5. He could have read the paper or watched the news so that he would know about the festival.
6. walking, taxi, subway, bicycle

pp. 152-153

1. c
2. She didn't have space for a garden so she started having potted plants in her apartment and developed a knack for it.
3. Answers will vary.
4. It is interesting because Rose's simple hobby grew into an award-winning project.
5. Answers will vary.

pp. 154-155

1. c
2. Answers will vary.
3. You don't have to buy gas, and it is a good workout.
4. garage sale, estate sale, grandmother's house
5. Take it to an antique dealer; look in an antique guide in the library; look on the Internet.
6. An antique dealer would not want the valuable item to be damaged because it might be worth a lot of money.
7. Answers will vary.

pp. 156-157

1. a. Wait for her neighbor to get home to help.
   b. Have the paper left just outside the door.
2. a, c, d, f
3. b
4. a, c, g, h, i
5. Answers will vary.

pp. 158-159

1. The tree-cutting companies are trying to get Willie to stop selling wood on the side of the road, but that is his only source of income.
2. a,d
3. promise to vote for the politicians in the next election, promise to advertise and promote local businesses and politicians with signs at his wood pile
4. Have one of the tree-cutting companies give Willie a job.
5. Answers will vary.

pp. 160-161

1. stamp collecting
2. Answers will vary.
3. She does research for her customers, buys and sells from all over the world, and teaches kids about stamp history.
4. surprised, shocked, taken aback
5. When she was a child she thought it was boring, but now she thinks it's exciting and interesting.
6. Answers will vary.

pp. 162-163

1. They think they're healthy; they think it's a waste of time.
2. d
3. You could overwork your heart and damage it; you could have trouble breathing.
4. muscle strain, join strain, head injury if you fall down, shoelace could get caught in the treadmill and cause you to fall
5. ask for help from an employee of the gym, get a personal trainer, read the manuals
6. muscle strain/tearing, neck injury, back injury, broken bones (if weights fall on you)
7. a. You could keep one another motivated.
   b. You won't get bored since you have someone to talk to.
   c. Your friend could help teach you how to use the equipment.

Note: Your clients' answers will vary on many of these tasks. Sample answers have been provided to assist you in cueing and modeling.

Answer Key

pp. 164-165

1. a, c, d, g, h
2. anger, frustration, worry, anxiety, fear
3. a, b, d, f, i, j, k
4. Answers will vary.

pp. 166-167

1. Many motorcycles look the same.
2. a fair, a meeting, an gathering
3. a. Put a bright sign on it.
   b. Remember where they parked it and make a note of it.
   c. Install a remote alarm.
4. b
5. Answers will vary.
6. Write down the section number, count the number of steps to the store doors, etc.
7. a. Wear a helmet.
   b. Be cautious of other vehicles on the road.
   c. Wear appropriate clothing for the weather.
   d. Drive carefully in dangerous road/weather conditions.
   e. Make visibility a priority.

p. 169

1. e
2. Your whole family may become aware of your dental problems; if you wanted to go to another dentist your family may be angry.
3. to make the same choices in life as someone older than you
4. Put aside your differences; talk about your problems and try to solve them together; compromise.
5. a. Count to 10 before getting angry.
   b. Instead of yelling, walk away.
   c. Talk calmly about their disagreements and try to resolve them.

pp. 170-171

1. a. family, old friends, and teammates were called
   b. built Bocce courts
   c. purchased Bocce balls
   d. collected Enzo's tournament memorabilia and displayed it
   e. made Enzo's favorite Italian foods
2. He was 75; he saw his old friends again; he was able to reenact a moment in his life that was important to him.
3. throwing a medium-sized ball to a designated spot on the court
4. to remember or to recall
5. Answers will vary.

p. 173

1. b, c
2. She couldn't say anything because she didn't know what to say.
3. Answers will vary.
4. He could have worked a second job or taught at a private school that paid well.
5. bad behavior of students, eventual dissatisfaction with his job, may miss being a stockbroker

pp. 174-175

1. He lives far away from them.
2. It is an electronic method of communicating using a computer and keyboard.
3. Answers will vary.
4. Answers will vary.
5. His grandchildren don't speak as clearly; the men have lower/louder voices.
6. letter, telegram, postcard, FAX, instant messaging, chat rooms, etc.

pp. 176-177

1. She can't fit everything in her new apartment.
2. a, b
3. to not be in use, to take up space, to be thrown away
4. Answers will vary.
5. give them to a homeless shelter, give them away to friends, etc.
6. Answers will vary.

p. 179

1. a. David leads a pretty quiet life.
   b. He's a 28-year-old bachelor.
2. She was late for her meetings; she was worried about Danny's safety with David; she was worried David would be upset or change his mind.
3. David, you're a lifesaver. I really appreciate you doing this for me. I'm already late for my meeting, so I can't tell you everything about Danny, but he needs to be changed.
4. He was able to have fun with Danny; he learned that it's not as scary as it seems.

21-05-98765432

Note: Your clients' answers will vary on many of these tasks. Sample answers have been provided to assist you in cueing and modeling.

